Maths Progres[s]

Depth Book

Series editors: Dr Naomi Norman and Katherine Pate
Author: Caroline Locke

Second Edition

2

Pearson

Published by Pearson Education Limited, 80 Strand, London, WC2R 0RL.

www.pearsonschoolsandfecolleges.co.uk

Text © Pearson Education Limited 2019
Project managed and edited by Just Content Ltd
Typeset by PDQ Digital Media Solutions Ltd
Original illustrations © Pearson Education Limited 2019
Cover illustration by Robert Samuel Hanson

The rights of Nick Asker, Jack Barraclough, Sharon Bolger, Lynn Byrd, Andrew Edmondson, Bobbie Johns, Caroline Locke, Catherine Murphy, Naomi Norman, Mary Pardoe, Katherine Pate, Harry Smith and Angela Wheeler to be identified as authors of this work have been asserted by them in accordance with the Copyright, Designs and Patents Act 1988.

First published 2019

22 21 20 19
10 9 8 7 6 5 4 3 2 1

British Library Cataloguing in Publication Data
A catalogue record for this book is available from the British Library.

ISBN 978 1 292 28001 1

Printed in Italy by L.E.G.O S.p.A

Acknowledgements
Text: p8: Lerwick, Shetland Islands, Uk Climate Graphs, © climatemps.com; **p68** Table showing life expectancy of men and women in Somalia for a 10-year period: Data from The World Bank, World Development Indicators, a Creative Commons Attribution 4.0 International License (CC BY 4.0).

Note from the publisher
Pearson has robust editorial processes, including answer and fact checks, to ensure the accuracy of the content in this publication, and every effort is made to ensure this publication is free of errors. We are, however, only human, and occasionally errors do occur. Pearson is not liable for any misunderstandings that arise as a result of errors in this publication, but it is our priority to ensure that the content is accurate. If you spot an error, please do contact us at resourcescorrections@pearson.com so we can make sure it is corrected.

Contents

Maths Progress Second Edition

Confidence at the heart

Maths Progress Second Edition is built around a unique pedagogy that has been created by leading mathematics educational researchers and Key Stage 3 teachers in the UK. The result is an innovative structure, based around 10 key principles designed to nurture confidence and raise achievement.

Pedagogy – our 10 key principles

- Fluency
- Problem-solving
- Reflection
- Mathematical Reasoning
- Progression
- Linking
- Multiplicative Reasoning
- Modelling
- Concrete - Pictorial - Abstract (CPA)
- Relevance

This edition of Maths Progress has been updated based on feedback from thousands of teachers and students.

The Core Curriculum

Textbooks with tried-and-tested differentiation

Core Textbooks *For your whole cohort*

Based on a single, well-paced curriculum with built-in differentiation, fluency, problem-solving and reasoning so you can use them with your whole class. They follow the unique unit structure that's been shown to boost confidence and support every student's progress.

Support Books
Strengthening skills and knowledge

Provide extra scaffolding and support on key concepts for each lesson in the Core Textbook, giving students the mathematical foundations they need to progress with confidence.

Depth Books
Extending skills and knowledge

Deepen students' understanding of key concepts, and build problem-solving skills for each lesson in the Core Textbook so students can explore key concepts to their fullest.

Welcome to Maths Progress Second Edition Depth Books!

Building confidence with depth of understanding

Pearson's unique unit structure in the Core Textbooks has been shown to build confidence. The Depth Books take elements of this structure and help students continue to grow in confidence.

Master → **Extend**

1 In the **Master** section of the Depth books, students can deepen their understanding of the key concepts introduced in the Core Textbooks through rich tasks involving problem-solving and reasoning.

2 Students who have developed fluency and a solid understanding of key concepts throughout the Depth unit can **extend** their learning.

Master
Deepen understanding of key mathematical concepts.

Unit opener
Lesson opener outlines lesson objectives.

Investigation
Rich, problem-solving tasks to encourage deep thinking and exploring mathematical concepts at students' own pace.

A wealth of problem-solving questions encouraging students to:
- think in different ways
- translate contextual information
- make choices about the best method or strategy (e.g. work backwards, draw a diagram).

Reasoning questions allow students to:
- practice constructing multiple chains of reasoning
- interpret and explain results
- understand how and why to apply certain mathematical processes.

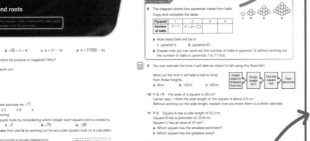

Reflect
Metacognitive questions that relate to the key concepts drawn out in each lesson, encouraging students to examine their thinking and understanding.

Hints
Guide students to help build problem-solving strategies throughout the course.

Extend
Students can take their understanding even further by applying what they have learned in different situations, and linking topics together.

This Depth Book is designed to give the right level of additional problem-solving content to help strengthen students' understanding of key concepts. It can be used as further stretch for students who are comfortable with the work in the Core Textbook Unit. Students who would benefit from additional scaffolding for key concepts can use the Support Book.

Progress with confidence!

This innovative Key Stage 3 Mathematics course builds on the first edition KS3 Maths Progress (2014) course, drawing on input from thousands of teachers and students, and a 2-year study into the effectiveness of the course. All of this has come together with the latest cutting-edge approaches to shape Maths Progress Second Edition.

Take a look at the other parts of the series

*Active*Learn Service

The *Active*Learn service enhances the course by bringing together your planning, teaching and assessment tools, as well as giving students access to additional resources to support their learning. Use the interactive Scheme of Work, linked to all the teacher and student resources, to create a personalised learning experience both in and outside the classroom.

What's in ActiveLearn for Maths Progress?

- ☑ **Front-of-class student books** with links to PowerPoints, videos, animations and homework activities

- ☑ **96 new KS3 assessments and online markbooks,** including end-of-unit, end-of-term and end-of-year tests

- ☑ **Over 500 editable and printable homework worksheets** linked to each lesson and differentiated for Support, Core and Depth

- ☑ **Online, auto-marked homework activities**

- ☑ **Interactive Scheme of Work** makes re-ordering the course easy by bringing everything together into one curriculum for all students with links to Core, Support and Depth resources, and teacher guidance

- ☑ **Student access to videos, homework and online textbooks**

ActiveLearn Progress & Assess

The Progress & Assess service is part of the full ActiveLearn service, or can be bought as a separate subscription. It includes assessments that have been designed to ensure all students have the opportunity to show what they have learned through:

- a 2-tier assessment model
- approximately 60% common questions from Core in each tier
- separate calculator and non-calculator sections
- online markbooks for tracking and reporting
- mapped to indicative 9–1 grades

New *Assessment Builder*

Create your own classroom assessments from the bank of Maths Progress assessment questions by selecting questions on the skills and topics you have covered. Map the results of your custom assessments to indicative 9–1 grades using the custom online markbooks. *Assessment Builder* is available to purchase as an add-on to *Active*Learn Service or Progress & Assess subscriptions.

Purposeful Practice Books

Over 3,750 questions using minimal variation that:

- ✓ build in small steps to consolidate knowledge and boost confidence
- ✓ focus on strengthening skills and strategies, such as problem-solving
- ✓ help every student put their learning into practice in different ways
- ✓ give students a strong preparation for progressing to GCSE study.

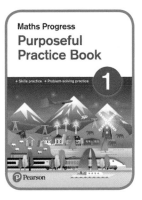
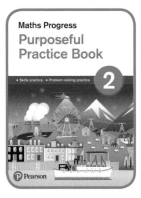
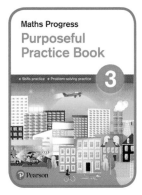

1 Number

Master   Extend p13

1.1 Calculations

- Use written methods to add and subtract more than two numbers (including decimals)
- Use mental calculation for multiplication
- Estimate answers to calculations

1 Georgina wants to buy four calculators for her friends.
The calculators cost £6.35 each.
Georgina has £25. Use estimation to decide if Georgina has enough money.

2 Lara owes £28 300 on her mortgage.
She repays £12 485 using her savings and a further £9100 from selling her car.
a How much does Lara still owe on her mortgage?
b She repays the remaining mortgage in 12 equal monthly instalments.
Work out her monthly instalment to the nearest penny.

3 The distance d km a train travels in t hours at a speed of s km/h is
given by the formula $d = st$.
Estimate the distance a train travels in 2.55 hours at a speed of 310 km/h.

4 Use estimation to decide which one of these calculations is incorrect.
a $3480 - 18 \times 122 = 2284$ **b** $(8.3 + 11.8) \times (15.8 - 10.9) = 98.49$
c $27 \times 48 \div 72 = 18$

5 Work out:
a $0.45 + 0.28 - 0.61$ **b** $0.45 - 0.61 + 0.28$
c R What do you notice? Will this always happen? Explain.
d Work out $0.75 - 0.96 + 0.25$.

6 R Use the fact that $31 \times 12 = 372$ to calculate 15×15.

7 P-S Tom takes out a loan for £6724.
He has to pay £672.40 interest on top of the amount of the loan.
Tom pays back £135 each week for 7 weeks.
He then decides to finish paying off the loan in 20 more weeks.
He decides to pay in equal weekly instalments.
How much will he have to pay each week?

8 **P-S / R** For each part, use all of the digits 1, 2, 3, 4, 5 once each and no other digits. Show working to explain your answers.

Q8 hint You can make numbers using the digits, e.g. 15 or 523, as well as using single digits such as 5.

   a Using only subtraction, write a calculation that will give the answer 0.

   b What is the largest positive integer you can make from a calculation using only subtraction?

Q8b hint An **integer** is a whole number.

   c What is the largest positive integer you can make using only addition?

   d What is the smallest positive integer you can make using only addition?

   e What is the largest positive integer you can make using only multiplication?

   f What is the smallest positive integer you can make from using only multiplication?

9 **P-S** Markus is baking cupcakes for 72 people.
The recipe for 12 cupcakes needs 110 g of butter, 110 g of caster sugar, 2 eggs and 110 g of flour.
Eggs are sold in boxes of 6, which weigh 438 g.
The other ingredients are sold in 500 g and 1 kg amounts.
A shopping bag can hold 7.7 kg.
How many bags will Markus need to carry the ingredients home from the shop?

10 **P-S** In this addition pyramid, each brick is the sum of the two bricks below it.

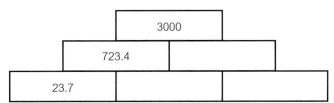

What is the difference between the two missing numbers on the bottom row?

Investigation

11 **a** Estimate 34 × 57 by rounding both numbers up.
    This will give you an **overestimate**.

   b Estimate 34 × 57 by rounding both numbers down.
    This will give you an **underestimate**.

   c Estimate 34 × 57 by rounding one number up and one number down.

   d Repeat part **c** rounding the numbers the opposite way.

   e Which estimate do you think is closest to the exact answer?
    Check to see if you are right.

   f Repeat parts **a–e** using two different 2-digit numbers.
    Write a rule for making the closest estimate.

Reflect

12 Explain why 35 × 8 gives the same answer as 7 × 4 × 10.

Use this idea to describe how you could make a difficult multiplication such as 18 × 16 easier to work out.

1.2 Divisibility and division

- Know and use divisibility rules

1 **P-S / R** A number is divisible by 6 and 9, but not by 5.
It is less than 40, but greater than 30. What is the number?

2 **P-S** Write a 3-digit number that is divisible by both 5 and 3, but not by 2.

3 **P-S / R** You are given the digits 5, 6, 7, 8 and 9.
  a Make a 2-digit number that is divisible by 3, but not by 2.
  b Make a 3-digit number that is in the 9 times table.
  c Make a number with at least three factors, not including 1 and itself.
  d Why is it impossible to make a number divisible by both 5 and 2 from those digits?
  e Is it impossible to use those digits to make a 5-digit number that is divisible by 3?
    Give reasons.
  f Is it possible to fill in $\square\,\square \div \square = \square$ using just the digits given?
    Show your calculations.
  g Repeat parts **a–f** using the digits 0, 1, 2, 3 and 4.
    What is the same and what is different?

4 **P-S / R** Find the missing numbers.

  a $\quad \square 14$
    $3 \overline{)\, 9\square 2}$

  b $\quad 436$
    $\square \overline{)\, 87\square}$

  c $\quad 032$
    $1\square \overline{)\, 384}$

5 **P-S / R** Arne bought a computer. The computer cost £2435.
He paid a deposit on the computer and then paid the rest in seven equal monthly instalments. The monthly instalments were integers.
  a What is the smallest deposit Arne could have paid?
  b What would his monthly payments be?

6 **R** Mashrur is thinking of a number that rounds to 110 to the nearest ten.
It is divisible by 7 but not by 2. What is the number?

7 **R** What fraction of numbers that are divisible by 6 are also divisible by 9? Explain.

8 **P-S / R** A set of five numbers has a mean that is divisible by 9.
Two of the numbers are in the 3 times table, but not the 9 times table.
One of the numbers is divisible by 8.
None of the numbers are divisible by 5.
None of the numbers are greater than 50.
What could the numbers be?

9 **P-S** Imrana works out the answer to a division and rounds it to the nearest integer.
She says her answer is 14.
She has spilled water on her work and can only see part of the question.

$204 \div 1$$.6$

What was the full calculation?

10 **R** Nazim has a number that is in the 6 times table.
He knows it is also divisible by 7.
Explain how Nazim knows that the number must be divisible by 42.

11 **R** A number is divisible by 12 and also divisible by 16.
Does the number have to be divisible by 12 × 16? Explain.

12 **R** Helen wants to know if 83 is a prime number. She works out an approximate answer for
the square root and then runs the divisibility tests for all the prime numbers less than this.
a Using this test, is 83 prime?
b Why does Helen only test all the prime numbers less than the approximate square root?
c Use this method to work out if 37 is prime.
d Use this method to work out if 117 is prime.

13 A deficient number is a number where the sum of its factors (excluding itself) is smaller
than the number itself. For example, 21 has the factors 1, 3 and 7, which sum to 11.
11 is smaller than 21, so 21 is a deficient number.
a Is 27 a deficient number?
b Is 36 a deficient number?
c **R** Are all prime numbers deficient numbers?

14 Factorial numbers are found by multiplying consecutive integers, starting at 1.
For example, 3 × 2 × 1 = 6, so 6 is a factorial number.
a Is 24 a factorial number?
b Is 120 a factorial number?
c **R** Will a factorial number ever be a square number? Explain.

Investigation

15 Choose a large number in the 13 times table. For example, 728.
Multiply the units digit by 4. For example, 4 × 8 = 32.
Add the result to the remaining number. For example, 32 + 72 = 104.
Check to see if this new number is divisible by 13.
What do you notice? Does this always work?

Reflect

16 Explain how knowing that a number is in both the 6 times table and the 9 times table also
lets you know that it is in the 18 times table.

1.3 Calculating with negative integers

- Add, subtract, multiply and divide positive and negative numbers, including larger numbers and decimals

1   A house has solar panels to generate electricity.
    When it doesn't generate enough electricity, it uses electricity from the national grid.
    When it generates too much it sends electricity back to the national grid.
    The table shows the electricity sent to the national grid every 10 minutes for one hour.

Time	14:00	14:10	14:20	14:30	14:40	14:50
Electricity (power, W)	−130	220	−1395	640	−1565	−290

   a Why is the power sometimes negative?

   Work out:

   b the median   **c** the range   **d** the mean.

2   Work out:
    a −3 × 2 × 4   **b** 5 × −3 × −2
    c −7 × −3 × −10   **d** −14 × −3 × −5

3   Work out:
    a 1.4 × −3   **b** −0.7 × −3 × −10
    c 10.5 × −3.2   **d** −3 × 2 × 0.5

4   Work out:
    a −4(−3.4 − −1.7)   **b** −4(−3.4 − 1.7)
    c −4 − 3.4 + 1.7   **d** −3.4 − −1.7 − 4

5   Work out:
    a 250 × −320 ÷ −800   **b** 0.5(−75 000 + −350 000 ÷ −2)
    c 24 000(−2 × 0.9 + 300 ÷ −1500)   **d** −100 000(0.13 − −0.38) ÷ −(6 ÷ 2)

6   **P-S**   Juan writes a question that gives
    the calculation 3 × −15 = −45.

   > Anna and John are divers.
   > Anna dives 3 times as deep as John.
   > John dives 15 m below sea level.
   > How deep does Anna dive?

   Write a question that gives this calculation:
      4 × −25 = −100

   > **Q6 hint** The question could
   > be about money, temperature,
   > distance below sea level,
   > ground level, etc.

7   The first term of a sequence is 4 and the term-to-term rule is 'multiply by −2'.
    a Write the first five terms of the sequence.
    b Work out the difference between the second and fourth terms.

8 **P-S / R** The answer to a calculation is −12.
Write four different calculations that each give an answer of −12.
Use each sign +, −, ×, ÷ at least once.

9 **R** The table shows the average minimum temperature
in 10 cities in January.
a Work out the range in temperatures.
b Work out the mean temperature.
Plymouth has a minimum temperature of 5°C.
Bucharest has a minimum temperature of −5°C.
These two cities are added to the list.
c How do these two temperatures affect the range you
found in part **a**?
d How do these two temperatures affect the mean you
found in part **b**?

City	Temperature (°C)
Budapest	−4
Canberra	13
Ellsworth	−18
Harare	17
Imst	−6
Madrid	3
Nuuk	−11
Oslo	−7
Ottawa	−14
Stanley	7

10 In the spider diagram, the four calculations give the answer in the middle.

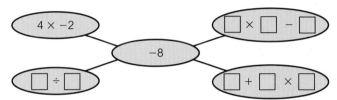

Work out three possible sets of missing values.

11 **P-S** The product of two numbers is 24.
The sum of the two numbers is negative. What could the numbers be?

12 **P-S** The answer to the division of two numbers is 2.
The sum of the two numbers is −12. What could the numbers be?

13 **P-S** The product of two numbers is negative.
The sum of the two numbers is greater than 5. What could the numbers be?

14 **P-S** The product of three numbers is 3. One of the numbers is −3.
What could the other two numbers be?

15 **P-S** The product of four numbers is 12. One of the numbers is −12.
What could the other three numbers be?

Reflect

16 More than two numbers are multiplied together.
Some are positive and some are negative.
How can you tell whether the answer will be positive or negative?
For example, if you multiply three numbers together and two are negative and one is
positive, will the answer be positive or negative?

1.4 Powers and roots

- Calculate using squares, square roots, cubes and cube roots
- Give integers that a square root lies between

1 Work out:

a $4 \times 3^2 + 5$ **b** $\sqrt{49} + 5 \times 8$ **c** $6 \times 2^3 - 18$ **d** $4 \times \sqrt[3]{1000} - 35$

2 **R** Can square numbers be positive or negative? Why?

3 Use a calculator to work out:

a $7^3 + 27$
b $2 \times 8^3 - 624$
c $6 \times 10^3 - 4 \times 9^3$
d $4 \times \sqrt[3]{729} + 4$
e $4 \times \sqrt[3]{216} - 5^2$

4 **a** **R** Choose the best estimate for $\sqrt{11}$.

3   3.1   3.5   3.9   4

Explain your reasoning.

b Estimate these square roots by considering which integer each square root is closest to.

i $\sqrt{20}$ **ii** $\sqrt{5}$ **iii** $\sqrt{79}$ **iv** $\sqrt{90}$

c Check your estimates from part **b** by working out the accurate square roots on a calculator.

5 **P-S** A wire fence surrounds a square playground with area $115\,\text{m}^2$.
On one side the wire is removed and replaced with a wooden fence.
The removed piece of wire fence is used to enclose a square garden.
Estimate the length of the garden.

> **Q5 hint** Draw diagrams to help you.

6 **R** Oliver planted some trees in a square plot of land with area $800\,\text{m}^2$.

a Estimate the length of the side of the plot.
b Oliver worked out the exact length of a side of the plot and rounded the answer to the nearest metre. He ordered four times this length of fencing to surround the plot.
  i Should Oliver have ordered this length of fencing? Explain your answer.
  ii Fencing is sold by the metre.
    How much fencing should Oliver have ordered?

7 **R** The area of a square is $100\,\text{cm}^2$.
Amisha says 'The side length of the square could be 10 cm or −10 cm.'
Jaya says 'The side length of the square can only be 10 cm.'
Who is correct? Explain your answer.

8 The diagram shows four pyramids made from balls.

Copy and complete the table:

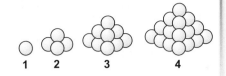

1   **2**   **3**   **4**

Pyramid	1	2	3	4
Number of balls	$1^2 = 1$	$1^2 + 2^2 = \square$		

a How many balls will be in

  i pyramid 5   **ii** pyramid 6?

b Explain how you can work out the number of balls in pyramid 12 without working out the number of balls in pyramids 1 to 11 first.

9 You can estimate the time it will take an object to fall using this flowchart.

Work out the time it will take a ball to drop from these heights.

a 80 m   **b** 125 m   **c** 405 m

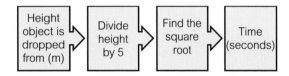

10 P-S / R The area of a square is 28 cm².
Lamar says, 'I think the side length of the square is about 4.8 cm.'
Without working out the side length, explain how you know there is a better estimate.

11 P-S Square A has a side length of 6.5 cm.
Square B has a perimeter of 25.6 cm.
Square C has an area of 47 cm².

a Which square has the smallest perimeter?

b Which square has the greatest area?

12 Sort these cards into matching pairs.

$14 + 4^2$	$14 - 4^2$	$14 + (-4)^2$	$14 - (-4)^2$

$25 - 2^2 - 6^2$	$25 - (-2)^2 + 6^2$	$25 - 2^2 + (-6)^2$	$25 - 2^2 - (-6)^2$

13 R The area of a square is 50 cm². Explain why it cannot have integer side lengths.

14 R a Is each calculation true or false? Give reasons for your answers.

  i $\sqrt{36} = \sqrt{9} \times \sqrt{4}$ **ii** $\sqrt{13} = \sqrt{9} + \sqrt{4}$

  iii $\sqrt{5} = \sqrt{9} - \sqrt{4}$ **iv** $\dfrac{\sqrt{100}}{\sqrt{25}} = \sqrt{4}$

b Re-write $\sqrt{144}$ as the product of two other square roots.

15 When does it not make sense to use the negative solution to the square root of a positive number?

> **Hint** Look back at the questions you have answered in this section to help you.

1.5 Powers, roots and brackets

- Calculate combinations of squares, square roots, cubes, cube roots and brackets

1 Work out:

  a $\sqrt{1600}$ **b** $\sqrt{2500}$ **c** $\sqrt{12\,100}$

  d $\sqrt{90\,000}$ **e** $\sqrt{4\,000\,000}$ **f** $\sqrt{360\,000}$

 Q1 hint $1600 = 16 \times 100$

 2 Work out:

  a $\sqrt[3]{11^2 + 2^2}$ **b** $\dfrac{20 + 50}{\sqrt[3]{20 \times 50}}$

3 Work out:

  a $\dfrac{6^2}{4} - 15$ **b** $\dfrac{\sqrt{100}}{2} + 10^2$ **c** $\dfrac{10^3}{500}$

  d $\dfrac{40}{2^3}$ **e** $\dfrac{24}{\sqrt[3]{8}}$ **f** $\dfrac{20}{\sqrt[3]{125}} - 2^2$

4 Give both solutions to each calculation. The first one is done for you.

  a $\sqrt{31 - 2 \times 3}$ **b** $\sqrt{6 \times 5 - 14}$ **c** $\sqrt{7 \times 6 - 3 \times 11}$

    $= \sqrt{31 - 6}$

    $= \sqrt{25}$

    $= 5 \text{ or } -5$

5 Estimate the answer to:

  a $\dfrac{(1.2 + 3.5)^2}{1.8^3}$ **b** $\dfrac{(27 - 14)^3}{7.3^2}$ **c** $\dfrac{(3.3^2 \times 2)}{(2.3 + 4.2)^2}$ **d** $\dfrac{(786 - 529)^2}{7.4^2}$

6 **R** Here are some numbers: 1   2   3   4   5   6

  What numbers can you use so that $(\Box + \Box)^2 + (\Box - \Box)^3$

  a has the biggest possible answer   **b** has the smallest possible answer?

 7 **P-S**

  a Match each calculation card with the correct answer card.
    Check your answers using a calculator.

     $\sqrt{3^3 + 3^2}$ $13 - (\sqrt[3]{125} + 3)$  $8 \times (11 - \sqrt[3]{1000})$ $\sqrt[3]{40 + 24}$

    4   5   6   7   8

  b There is one answer card left over. Write a calculation to go with this answer.
    The calculation must include a cube root or a square root.

8 Here are four number cards.

$$\sqrt{7^2 + 15} \qquad 20 - (4 + \sqrt[3]{64}) \qquad 6 \times (\sqrt[3]{27} + 2^2) \qquad \sqrt[3]{6^2 - 44}$$

    a Work out the mean of the values on the number cards.

    b Work out the range of the values on the number cards.

9 **P-S** The sum of these two values is 8.
Work out the missing number.

$$\frac{32 + \square}{5^2} \qquad \frac{45 - \sqrt{81}}{2 \times 3}$$

10 **R** The energy of an object is related to its mass and velocity.
Jenny is working out the energy of different roller coaster cars.
She uses the rule

$$\text{Energy} = \frac{\text{mass} \times \text{velocity}^2}{2}$$

Roller coaster car	A	B	C
Mass (kg)	450	625	450
Velocity (m/s)	20	38	40

    a Work out the energy for each car.

    b Car C has the same mass as Car A.

       Its velocity is twice as fast.

       Does it have twice as much energy?

11 **a** Work out the missing number. $\quad \dfrac{\sqrt[3]{\square} \times 3}{3^2} = 1$

    b Write two more calculations using the same idea. $\quad \dfrac{\sqrt[3]{\square} \times \square}{\square^2} = 1$

12 Calculate $3^2 \times 2^2$ and 6^2.

    a What do you notice?

    b Does this work for $3^3 \times 2^3$ and 6^3?

    c **R** Is there an integer power of 6 for $3^2 \times 2^3$? Give reasons.

13 **a** Calculate $3^2 + 2^2$, 5^2, and $(3 + 2)^2$. What do you notice?

    b Calculate $3^2 + 4^2$, 5^2 and $(3 + 4)^2$. What do you notice?

    c Calculate $4^2 + 5^2$ and 6^2. Does the pattern continue?

14 **P-S** Place brackets into the calculation $5 + 3^2$ so that it is equivalent to 8^2.

15 **P-S** Change the calculation $(2 + 5)^2$ so that it is equivalent to 343.

Investigation

16 Multiply two consecutive even numbers and add 1. Then find the square root.
What do you notice? Is this always true? Does this work for consecutive odd numbers?

Reflect

17 You were asked to write a calculation in Q11 including a cube root and a square that
gave a specific integer answer.
What part of the calculation did you write first? Explain why.

1.6 More powers, multiples and factors

- Use index notation
- Write a number as the product of its prime factors
- Use prime factor decomposition to find the highest common factor (HCF) and lowest common multiple (LCM)

1 Work out:

   a 1.2^4 **b** $(-5)^4$

   c $\sqrt[3]{6.4}$ **d** $\sqrt[3]{-0.064}$

2 **a** Write down all the factors of:

     i 16
     ii 40
     iii 56

  b Write down the HCF of 16, 40 and 56.

3 **a** Write down the first 10 multiples of:

     i 3
     ii 4
     iii 6

  b Write down the LCM of 3, 4 and 6.

4 The CN Tower in Toronto is 1815 ft tall.
Write this height as a product of its prime factors using index notation.

5 **P-S** Here are some prime factor decomposition cards.

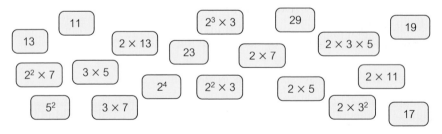

The cards represent the numbers from 10 to 30.
Two of the cards are missing.
What is the prime factor decomposition on each of the missing cards?

6 **P-S** The train to Wolverhampton leaves every 20 minutes.
The train to Ashminster leaves every 24 minutes.
They both leave at 9:00 am.
Use the lowest common multiple to find out when they next both leave at the same time.

7 **P-S** Ellen is working out the prime factor decomposition of a number.
She draws this factor tree.

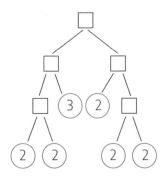

What is Ellen's number?

8 **a** Work out the prime factor decomposition of these numbers.
 i 165
 ii 180
 iii 210
b What is the HCF of 165, 180 and 210?
c What is the LCM of 165, 180 and 210?

9 **P-S** A number is written as a product of its prime factors:
23 × 3^2 × a
The number is in the 15 times table.
What must a be?

10 **P-S** The highest common factor of two numbers is 18.
One of the numbers is in the 5 times table.
The other number is in the 7 times table.
What could the numbers be?

11 **P-S / R** The highest common factor of two numbers is 15.
One of the numbers is even.
Explain why the other number must be odd.

12 **P-S / R** The LCM of two numbers is
11^2 × 13 × 15^3 × 17^4 × 29 × 31^5
The HCF of the two numbers is
11^2 × 15
One of the two numbers is
11^2 × 15^3 × 17^4
What is the other number?

Reflect

13 Are there any numbers that cannot be written as a product of prime factors? Explain.

1 Extend

1　**P-S / R**　A 3-digit number is divided by 8 with no remainder.

   a　The final digit of the answer is 5.

     What was the last digit of the 3-digit number?

   b　The same 3-digit number is divided by 5.
     The last two digits of the answer are 68.
     What is the second digit of the number?

   c　The sum of the digits of the 3-digit number is in the 6 times table.
     What is the number?

2　**P-S**　The sum of three consecutive square numbers is an odd multiple of 5, and 2 more than a multiple of 9.
   What is the cube root of the sum of the positive square roots of the three numbers?

3　**P-S**　How many integers between 100 and 200 end in 9 and are in the 3 times table?
   Compare this to the number of integers between 200 and 300.
   Is it the same or different?

4　**P-S**　The volume of a solid is $297 \, \text{cm}^3$.
   The solid is composed of cubes with integer side lengths.
   One cube has no faces on the outside of the solid.
   Six cubes show five faces each.
   The remaining cubes only show four faces.
   What is the surface area of the solid?

5　**P-S**　Place the numbers −4, −2, −1, 0, 0, 1, 2, 3, 4 into the grid so that every row and column has the same sum.

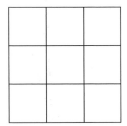

6　**P-S**　The sum of the digits of the number ABCDE is divisible by 7.
   Each consecutive pair of digits in ABCDE is a square number (so AB is a square number, BC is a square number, and so on).
   What is this number?

7 The table shows the number of days it takes four of the planets in our solar system to orbit the Sun.

Planet	Number of days to orbit the Sun	Prime factor decomposition
Mercury	88	88 =
Earth	365	365 =
Uranus	30 700	30 700 =
Neptune	60 200	60 200 =

a Copy and complete the table.

Assume that on one day, all four planets are in alignment with the Sun.

b How many days will it be before these planets are aligned with the Sun again?

   i Uranus and Neptune

   ii Earth and Uranus

   iii Uranus and Mercury

   iv Mercury and Neptune

> **Q7b hint** Draw a diagram of the Sun and the four planets.

c Which two planets will take the longest time to align with the Sun again?

d How many days will it be before Uranus, Mercury and Neptune are aligned with the Sun again?

8 **P-S / R** The first two digits of an integer form a number that is divisible by 9 but not by 2.
The second two digits form a number that is divisible by 2 but not by 3.
The last digit is an 8.
The whole number is divisible by 9, 2, 3 and 7.
What could the number be?

Investigation

9 Take the numbers 248 and 492.
   Step 1: Divide the larger number by the smaller, leaving the remainder.
   Step 2: Divide the smaller of the original numbers by the remainder.
   Step 3: Divide your answer to step 1 by the remainder from step 2.
Continue this process until the remainder is 0.
What have you calculated? Does this work for any pair of numbers? Why?

Investigation

10 A Mersenne prime is a prime number that is found by calculating 2^p and then subtracting 1, where p is a prime number.

a How many primes under 100 are Mersenne primes?

b Is every number that you calculate using the formula a prime number?

Reflect

11 Imagine you are working out calculations without using a calculator.
What steps can you take to try to ensure your answers are correct?

2 Area and volume

Master   Extend p27

2.1 Area of a triangle

- Derive and use the formula for the area of a triangle
- Calculate the area of compound shapes made from rectangles and triangles

1 Work out the area of each triangle.

a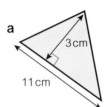

b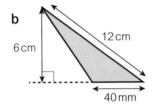

c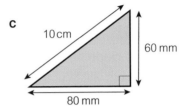

2 **P-S** Draw as many right-angled triangles as you can with an area of $12\,\text{cm}^2$.
How will you know when you have drawn them all?

> **Q2 hint** Use whole number lengths only.

3 **P-S / R** A triangle has a base $2\,\text{cm}$ and an area of $18\,\text{cm}^2$.
   a What is the perpendicular height?
   b Do you have enough information to draw an accurate sketch of this triangle?

4 A rectangle has an area of $20\,\text{cm}^2$.
   The rectangle is split into four congruent triangles.
   a What is the area of each triangle?
   b The base length and perpendicular height of each triangle have integer values.
      i What is the length of the base?
      ii What is the perpendicular height?
   c What type of triangles are they?
   d What are the possible dimensions of the original rectangle?

5 **P-S** Work out the shaded area.

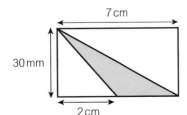

6 Work out the shaded area of each shape.

a

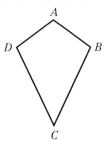

7 cm

14 cm

b

3 cm

4 cm

5 cm

5 cm

5 cm

7 P-S / R The kite *ABCD* has length *AC* = 12 cm and length *BD* = 4 cm.

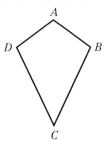

A

D

B

C

> **Q7a hint** You can split the kite into triangles.

a Calculate the area of the kite.

b A rectangle is drawn with half of the area of the kite.
One of the side lengths is the same as the length *DB* on the kite.
What is the other side length of the rectangle?

c A triangle is drawn with the same area as the kite.
One of the side lengths is the same as the length *DB* on the kite.
What is the perpendicular height of the triangle?

8 P-S / R *ABCD* is a square with side length 6 cm.
The ratio *AE* : *ED* is 2 : 1.

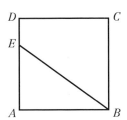

D *C*

E

A *B*

a What fraction of the total area is taken up by triangle *ABE*?

b The side length of the square is changed. Does the fraction change? Explain.

Reflect

9 You are told the area of a shape.
How many possible squares can you draw with this area?
How many triangles can you draw with this area?

> **Hint** Look back at your answers to Q2 and Q3.

2.2 Area of a parallelogram and trapezium

- Derive and use the formula for the area of a parallelogram
- Use the formula for the area of a trapezium

1 R

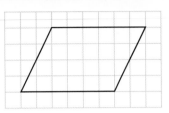

a Copy this parallelogram on squared paper.

b Calculate the area of the parallelogram.

c Split the parallelogram in half to make two triangles.

d What is the area of one of the triangles?

e Complete the formulae:

Area of triangle =   Area of parallelogram =

2 Work out the missing measurement for each shape.

a

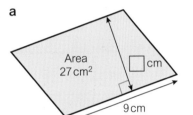

Area 27 cm²

☐ cm

9 cm

b

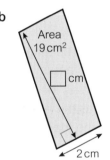

Area 19 cm²

☐ cm

2 cm

c

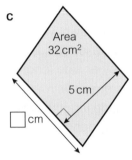

Area 32 cm²

5 cm

☐ cm

3 Write two different calculations for the area of this parallelogram.

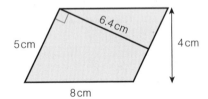

6.4 cm

5 cm

4 cm

8 cm

4 Write an expression for the area of each parallelogram. Write each answer in its simplest form.

a

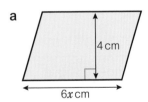

4 cm

$6x$ cm

b

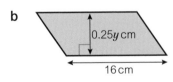

$0.25y$ cm

16 cm

5 Work out the area of each trapezium.

a

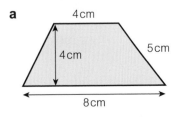

4 cm

4 cm

5 cm

8 cm

b

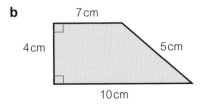

7 cm

4 cm

5 cm

10 cm

c

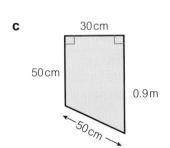

30 cm

50 cm

0.9 m

50 cm

6 **R** The diagram shows a trapezium.
Dave says, 'If I double the height of the trapezium,
the area of the trapezium will also double'.
Is he correct? Explain how you worked out your answer.

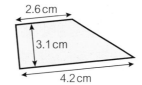

7 **P-S** This trapezium and this parallelogram have the same area.

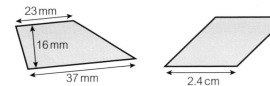

> **Q7 hint** Make sure
> all measurements are
> in the same units.

What is the perpendicular height of the parallelogram?

8 **P-S** The area of each trapezium is 20 cm².

a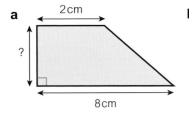

b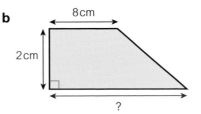

c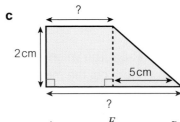

Calculate the missing lengths.

9 **P-S** Shape $ABCD$ is a square with side length 12 cm.
F is the midpoint of AD and G is the midpoint of BC.
E is a point that is two thirds of the way up AB.
GH is half the distance HF.
What is the area of shape $AEHF$?

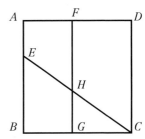

Investigation

10 The opposite sides of a quadrilateral are parallel and sum to 15 cm.
The perpendicular distance between these sides is 4 cm.

   a What is the area when the quadrilateral is a
   i rectangle **ii** trapezium **iii** parallelogram?

   b Draw a possible rectangle.
   How many possible rectangles are there with integer side lengths?

   c Draw a possible parallelogram.
   How many possible parallelograms are there with integer side lengths?

   d Draw a possible trapezium.
   How many possible trapeziums are there with integer side lengths?

Reflect

11 In each question you multiplied two lengths to calculate the area.
What is the relationship between the two lengths you multiplied each time?

2.3 Volume of cubes and cuboids

- Calculate the volume of cubes and cuboids
- Calculate the volume of shapes made from cuboids
- Solve volume problems

1 **R** Look at this cuboid.

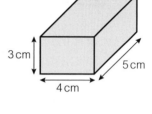

3 cm
5 cm
4 cm

a What is the volume of the cuboid?

b Write the dimensions of at least three
more cuboids with the same volume.

c Usman says a cuboid with dimensions $\frac{1}{2}$cm by 12 cm by 10 cm
has the same volume as this cuboid. Is he right?

d Are there more cuboids with the same volume?

2 **P-S** The volume of this cuboid is 168 cm³.
Work out the missing length.

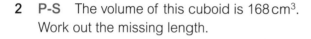

4 cm
6 cm
☐ cm

3 **P-S** A 3 cm by 3 cm by 3 cm cube has a 1 cm by 1 cm
square hole cut through it. What is the volume of the
remaining solid?

Q3 hint What is the
volume of the piece
cut out of the cube?

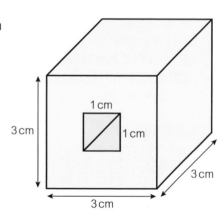

3 cm
1 cm
1 cm
3 cm
3 cm

4 **P-S**

a A 10 cm by 30 cm by 40 cm cuboid
is cut from a larger cuboid.
Calculate the volume of the remaining solid.

20 cm
10 cm
40 cm
30 cm
40 cm
60 cm

b This shape is made by cutting out a cuboid from
a 8 cm by 10 cm by 4 cm cuboid. Calculate

i the volume of the original cuboid

ii the volume of the cuboid cut out

iii the volume of the remaining solid.

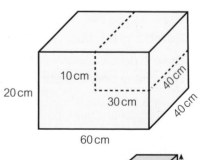
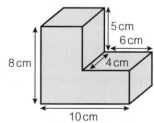

5 cm
6 cm
8 cm
4 cm
10 cm

5 P-S The volume of water in a fish tank is $84\,000\,cm^3$.
The fish tank has length 60 cm and width 35 cm.
The water comes to 10 cm from the top of the tank.
Calculate the height of the tank.

Q5 hint Sketch the water in the tank. Put the measurements you know on your sketch.

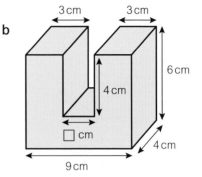

6 Calculate the volume of each solid.

a

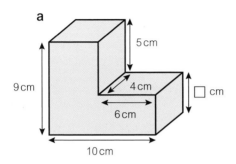

5 cm
9 cm
4 cm
6 cm
☐ cm
10 cm

b

3 cm   3 cm
6 cm
4 cm
☐ cm
4 cm
9 cm

c

6 cm
9 cm
2 cm
4 cm
☐ cm
8 cm

Q6 hint First calculate any missing lengths. Then divide the shape into cuboids and work out the volume of each cuboid separately.

7 P-S A flowerbed measures 4 m by 2 m. New soil is put on to add a depth of 5 cm.
A bag contains $12\,500\,cm^3$ of soil. How many bags of soil are needed?

Investigation

8 A cube has a volume of $64\,cm^3$.

a The side lengths of the cube are doubled.
What is the new volume?

b The side lengths of the original cube are tripled.
Predict the new volume then use a calculator to check your prediction.

c Continue to multiply the original lengths until you have a theory about what happens to the volume.

Reflect

9 a Why is area measured in square units?

b Why is volume measured in cube units?

Hint How many lengths do you multiply?

2.4 2D representations of 3D solids

- Sketch nets of 3D solids
- Draw 3D solids on isometric paper
- Draw plans and elevations of 3D solids

1 Here are two views of the same cuboid.
The second is drawn on isometric paper.

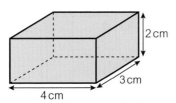
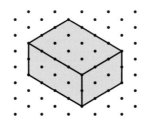

Draw these solids on isometric paper.

a

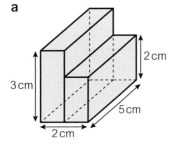

b

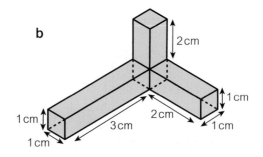

2 A 1 cm by 1 cm square hole is cut through the centre of each
face of this cube in all three directions. Draw the plan, front
elevation and side elevation.

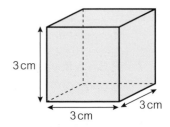

3 **R** **a** Draw the plan, the front elevation and the side elevation
of each solid on squared paper.

i
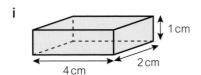

ii
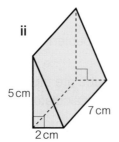

iii
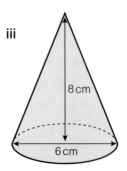

b For the solids in parts **a i** and **ii**, do the plans and elevations show

　i the shapes of all of the faces　　　**ii** the measurements of all of the faces?

c Draw an accurate net of the solid from part **a ii** on squared paper.
What are the measurements of the sloping face?

4   R   These solids are made from centimetre cubes.

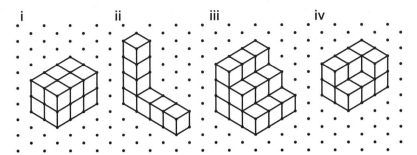

    a Draw the plan, front elevation and side elevation of each solid on squared paper.

    b What do you notice about your answers to part **a i** and **iv**?
       Why does this happen?

    c Do the plan, front and side elevations of the solids in part **a i** and **iv** give you enough information to make the solids from cubes?

5   P-S   Here are the plan, front and side elevations of an irregular 3D solid.

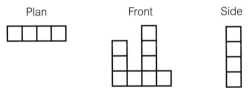

    Use cubes to make the solid. Then draw it on isometric paper.

6   P-S   Here is the side elevation of a 3D solid.
    Sketch three possible 3D solids it could belong to.

7   P-S / R   A solid is made from three red cubes, two blue cubes and one yellow cube.
    The solid is not a cuboid, and the blue cubes do not have faces touching.
    Charlie makes the solid and draws the plan view.
    He can see the yellow and blue cubes but not the red cubes in his plan view.
    Draw Charlie's solid on isometric paper.

8   P-S   Lauren wants to make as many 2 cm by 2 cm by 2 cm cubes as possible from a rectangle of paper measuring 24 cm by 30 cm.
    What is the maximum number of nets Lauren can cut out of the sheet of paper?

Reflect

9   R   In Q3, you were asked to draw the side elevations of a curved object.
    This diagram shows the side elevation of a 3D solid.

    a Is there enough information for you to identify the shape?
       Explain why or why not.

    b What other representation of this shape would give you more information?

2.5 Surface area of cubes and cuboids

- Calculate the surface area of cubes and cuboids

1 **P-S** Joey wants to wrap a present for his sister. Here are the measurements of the box and the wrapping paper:

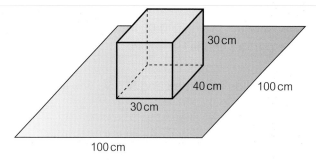

30 cm

40 cm　100 cm

30 cm

100 cm

Q1 hint Would a net of this box fit on the wrapping paper?

Does he have enough wrapping paper?

2 **P-S** Here are the areas of three faces of the same cuboid.

A
Area = 30 cm²

B
Area = 42 cm²

C
Area = 35 cm²

a What are the dimensions of each rectangle?
b What is the volume of the cuboid?
c What is the surface area of the cuboid?

Q3 hint Use the volume to work out the height of the cuboid first.

3 **P-S** A cuboid has a length of 3.6 m and a width of 2.5 m. Its volume is 37.8 m³. Work out the surface area of the cuboid.

4 **P-S** The diagram shows two cubes.
The side length of the larger cube is 4 cm.
The ratio of their surface areas is 1 : 4.
Work out:
a the surface area of the smaller cube
b the side length of the smaller cube.

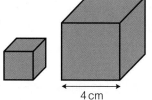

4 cm

Q4a hint Work out the surface area of the larger cube first.

5 **P-S** A red cuboid has length 6 cm, width 3 cm and height 2 cm. A blue cuboid has length 8 cm and width 2 cm. The red and blue cuboids have the same surface area. Work out the height of the blue cuboid.

Q5 hint Draw a sketch of each cuboid and label the missing height h. Then work out the surface area of the red cuboid.

6 a Calculate the surface area of each cuboid.

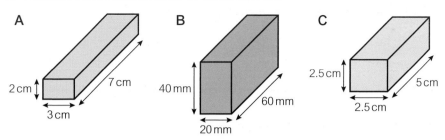

A — 2 cm, 7 cm, 3 cm

B — 40 mm, 60 mm, 20 mm

C — 2.5 cm, 5 cm, 2.5 cm

b R Imagine that the three cuboids are put together.

   i Will the volume of the new solid be the sum of the volumes?

   ii Will the surface area of the new solid be the sum of the surface areas?

   Explain your answers.

7 Calculate the surface area of each 3D solid.

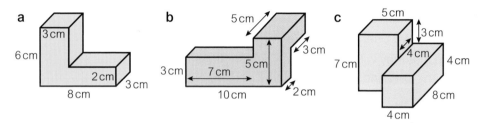

a — 3 cm, 6 cm, 2 cm, 3 cm, 8 cm

b — 5 cm, 3 cm, 3 cm, 5 cm, 7 cm, 2 cm, 10 cm

c — 5 cm, 3 cm, 4 cm, 7 cm, 4 cm, 8 cm, 4 cm

8 R These boxes have the same capacity.

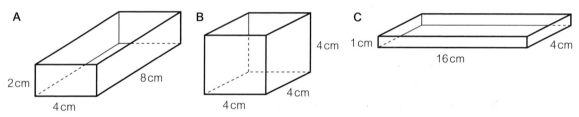

A — 2 cm, 8 cm, 4 cm

B — 4 cm, 4 cm, 4 cm

C — 1 cm, 16 cm, 4 cm

a Do they all have the same surface area?

b You run a packaging company. Which box would you choose and why?

c Here are the dimensions of three more boxes with the same capacity.

   3 cm × 24 cm × 3 cm   6 cm × 6 cm × 6 cm   4 cm × 9 cm × 6 cm

   Which box do you think would have the smallest surface area?

Investigation

9 A cuboid has a volume of 800 m^3. All of the lengths of the edges are integers.

   a What is the largest possible surface area?

   b What is the smallest possible surface area?

Reflect

10 a Is it possible for two cubes to have the same volume but different surface areas?

   b What about cuboids? Explain.

2.6 Measures

- Solve problems in everyday contexts involving measures
- Convert between different measures for area, volume and capacity
- Use tonnes and hectares
- Know rough metric equivalents of imperial measures

1 A premier league football pitch measures 105 m by 68 m.
An international rugby pitch measures 144 m by 70 m.
Work out the area of each pitch in **hectares**.

Q1 hint A hectare is 10 000 m².

2 A conservation trust has been given a 5.3 **hectare** piece of land. It plans
to use 18 750 m² for woodland and 28 125 m² for a wildlife meadow.
   a Is the area they have been given big enough for their planned use?
   b They estimate that they will need 2.4 m × 5 m sections for every 10 oak seedlings they
   plant. How many seedlings can they plant?

3 A rectangular reservoir measures 1.2 km by 1.6 km.
How many hectares is this?

4 a i Work out the area of this rectangle in cm².

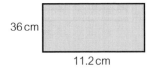

36 cm

11.2 cm

   ii Convert the area to mm².
   b Convert the lengths to mm and work out the area in mm².
   c R Which method was easier, the one in part **a** or part **b**?

5 The mass of 1 cm³ of water is approximately 1 g.
Estimate the mass of 1 cubic metre of water.

6 **P-S** Ann is surveying the plants growing in some wasteland,
measuring 7.5 m by 3.2 m. She places **quadrats** at random within the survey area.
Each quadrat is a 50 cm × 50 cm square.
   a What is the maximum number of quadrats that would fit?
   b She **samples** the plants in 12 quadrats randomly.
   None of the 12 quadrats overlap.
   What proportion of the wasteland has she sampled?

Q6 hint A **quadrat** is
a square frame used to
sample organisms, such
as plants, in a large area.

7 **P-S / R** Earthworms have been called 'ecosystem engineers'.
They improve soil structure and help release important nutrients to growing plants.
Fred reads that healthy soil should have 5600 earthworms per cubic metre.
He finds 40 earthworms in a 20 cm × 20 cm × 20 cm sample.
Is his sample healthy soil? Explain your answer.

8 **P-S** A container ship carries goods around the world.
A standard container is 40 ft long, 8 ft wide and
8 ft 6 inches high.

Q8 hint
1 ft = 12 inches
≈ 30 cm

  a Convert these measurements into centimetres.

  b Calculate the volume of the container in cubic centimetres.
The deck of a large ship measures 1200 ft long and 160 ft wide.

  c Approximately how many containers can fit into this area?

  d The ship can carry approximately 7500 containers.
How high will the containers be stacked?

  e Washing machines are packed in boxes 60 cm by 60 cm by 85 cm.
Each washing machine weighs 90 kg.
Calculate the weight of a container load of washing machines.

9 **P-S** Barry has a freezer with a capacity of 18 cubic feet.

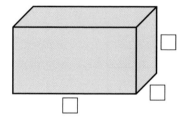

  a Write possible dimensions for the freezer in:

    i feet

    ii centimetres.

  b Calculate the capacity of the freezer in cubic centimetres.

Reflect

10 a What unit would you use to measure the weight of

    i a hamster

    ii a blue whale

    iii a sheep?

  b What unit would you use to measure the area of

    i a garden

    ii a playing field

    iii a laptop screen?

    Explain how you decided which units to use.

2 Extend

1 P-S The diagram shows a foldaway camping bowl.

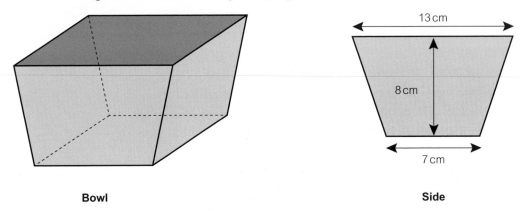

Bowl   **Side**

The bowl has four sides in the shape of congruent trapezia.
The bottom of the bowl is a square.
Work out the total surface area of the exterior of the bowl.

2 P-S / R *ABCD* is a rectangle.
E is the midpoint of *AD*.
AD is double *DC*.
The ratio *AF* : *BF* is 1 : 2.
FG is parallel to *AD*.
What fraction of *ABCD* is shaded?

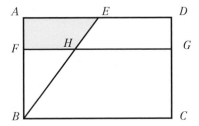

3 P-S James cuts fabric triangles with a base of 6 cm and a height of 5.2 cm.

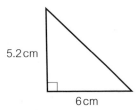

The fabric comes in rolls 50 cm wide, and costs £3.50 per metre length.
What is the least amount of money James can spend to cut 300 triangles?

4 **P-S / R** The diagram shows overlapping triangles *DFE* and *AFC*.

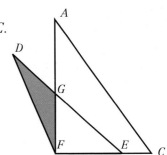

FE is $\frac{2}{3}$ the length of *FC*.

FC is $\frac{3}{4}$ the length *AF*.

The perpendicular height of the triangle *EFD* is equal to *FC*.

G is halfway between *F* and *A*.

FG = *FE*.

The area of triangle *FGE* is 4 cm².

Calculate the shaded area.

5 **P-S** A solid cube is made of metal and has a volume of 0.064 m³.

    a What is the length of the side in cm?

    b The cube is melted down and used to make a cuboid.
       10% of the material is wasted during the melting process.
       The cuboid has a square cross-section to make a cuboid 1 m tall.

       i A cube has the same cross-section as the cuboid.
         What is the volume of this cube?

       ii What is the surface area of the cuboid?

6 **P-S** There are 10 cubes arranged to make a shape.
Each cube has a volume of 125 cm³.
The surface area of the shape is 800 cm².
How many faces of the individual cubes are showing?

Investigation

7 Model a typical student from your class as a cuboid.

    a How many students do you think could stand in your classroom?

    b What assumptions have you made? Do you think they are good assumptions?

Investigation

8 Estimate the surface area of your classroom.
How will you estimate the height of the room with the greatest possible accuracy?
Start by drawing a plan view.
What are the most appropriate units of measurement?

Reflect

9 To describe a 2D shape, you can name the shape, or the shapes it is made from, draw a
diagram, and calculate its perimeter and area.
How can you describe a 3D solid?

3 Statistics, graphs and charts

Master   Extend p43

3.1 Pie charts

- Interpret pie charts
- Draw pie charts

1 The pie chart shows the different birds seen in a garden in one day.
In total, 72 birds were seen.
How many of them were

a starlings

b sparrows

c goldfinches?

Birds in a garden

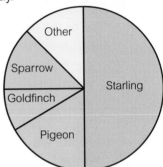

2 **P-S** For his geography project, Lee asked shoppers in the town centre how far they had travelled to the shops that day.

Distance travelled, d (miles)	Frequency
$0 \leqslant d < 3$	9
$3 \leqslant d < 6$	5
$6 \leqslant d < 9$	4
$9 \leqslant d < 12$	2

Q2 hint $0 \leqslant d < 3$ means that the distance travelled (d miles) can take any value from 0 up to but not including 3 miles.
$\leqslant$ means 'less than or equal to'.

a Draw a pie chart to show his data.

b Complete these sentences from Lee's report.

  i The modal distance travelled to the shops is _____.

  ii Fewer than half the shoppers had travelled less than _____.

  iii Just over 25% of shoppers had travelled more than _____.

3 The pie chart shows recommendations for healthy eating.
An active teenager needs about 2400 calories per day.
How many of these calories should be from

a non-dairy protein

b fruit and vegetables?

An active man needs 3000 calories per day.
How many of these calories should be from

c milk and dairy foods

d starchy foods?

Recommendations for healthy eating (calories)

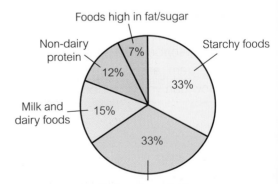

4 **P-S / R** The pie charts show a rock band's income in 2004 and 2014.

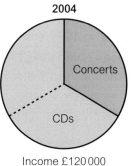

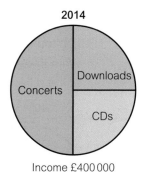

2004

2014

Income £120 000

Income £400 000

  a In 2004, $\frac{1}{3}$ of income was from concerts. How much did the band earn from concerts in 2004?

  b How much did the band earn from CDs in 2014?

  c Hedda says, 'The pie charts show that the band earned more from CDs in 2004 than in 2014.' Explain why she is wrong.

5 **P-S** The pie charts show Year 8 and Year 9 students' lunch choices.

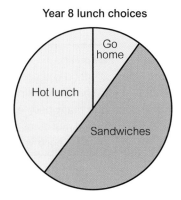

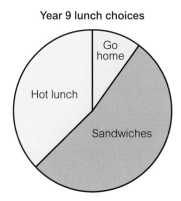

There are 180 students in Year 8 and 220 in Year 9.
Zoe says, 'More Year 9s than Year 8s go home for lunch.'
Is she correct? Show your working.

6 The pie charts show the energy generated by renewable technology in France and Germany in 2016.

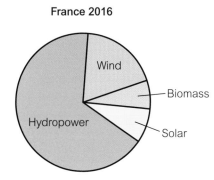

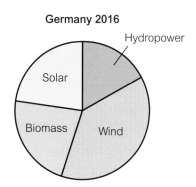

  a What fraction of energy was generated by
    i hydropower in France   **ii** biomass in Germany?

  b The total renewable energy generated in France in 2016 was 1 011 587 GWh. Estimate the energy generated by hydropower.

  c The total renewable energy generated in Germany in 2016 was 193 930 GWh. Estimate the energy generated by biomass.

  d **R** Compare the proportions of energy generated from each source for the two countries.

7 **R** The pie charts show visitor numbers for different British tourist attractions in 1981 and 1999.

   a Write three sentences comparing the percentages of visitors at the different attractions in 1981 and 1999.

Q7a hint
You might like to use some of these words: **increase, decrease, stayed the same**.

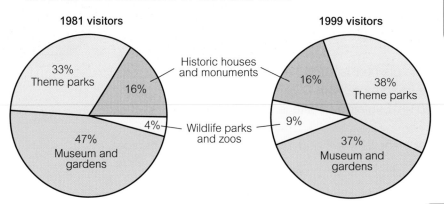

1981 visitors

33% Theme parks
16%
Historic houses and monuments
4% Wildlife parks and zoos
47% Museum and gardens

1999 visitors

16%
38% Theme parks
9%
37% Museum and gardens

   b A newspaper article commenting on these pie charts in 1999 said, 'More people visited museums and gardens in 1981 than in 1999.'

   Explain why this statement could be incorrect.

Q7b hint
What do you need to know to work out how many people visited museums and gardens each year?

8 **P-S** The pie charts show the languages studied by students in Year 10 in Schools A and B.

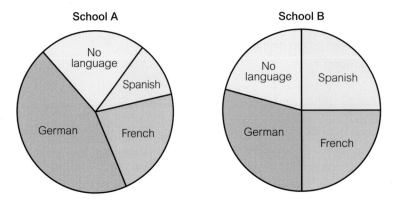

School A

No language
Spanish
German
French

School B

No language
Spanish
German
French

There are twice as many students who study French in School A than in School B.

There are 120 students in Year 10 in School B.

   a Which school has a greater proportion of students studying Spanish?

   b Which school has a greater proportion of students not studying a language?

   c How many Year 10 students are there in School A?

   d Which school has a greater number of students studying Spanish?

   e Which school has a greater number of students not studying a language?

Reflect

9 Francesca is comparing two pie charts.
   She says, 'The pie chart shows that more students take history at GCSE in School A than in School B.'
   Explain the problem with Francesca's statement.

3.2 Using tables

- Calculate the mean from a frequency table
- Design and use two-way tables
- Design and use tables for grouped data

1 Students from three different schools were asked which charity they would prefer to raise money for. The tally chart shows the results.

	Oxfam	Save the Children	RSPCA	Age UK
St Mary	卌	卌 |	卌 |	|||
Chilbrook	||	卌 ||||	卌 ||	||||
Oakmead	|||	||||	卌 卌	|||

a Copy and complete the compound bar chart.

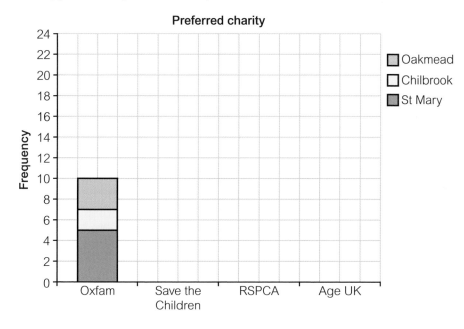

b How many students at Chilbrook answered the questionnaire?

c At which school did the RSPCA receive the most votes?

d Which charity received the most votes overall?

2 **P-S** A pizza takeaway asks its customers, 'Which is your favourite pizza?'
These are the possible options:

9" margherita	12" four cheese
12" pepperoni	12" margherita
9" four cheese	9" pepperoni

> **Q2 hint** 9" means 9 inches.

Design a table that the takeaway could use to record customers' choices.

3 R This data shows the shoe sizes in a Year 7 class.

3, 3, 3, 4, 4, 5, 5, 5, 5, 6, 6

a What are the mean, median and mode of the shoe sizes?

b Which average do you think best represents the data and why?

c The table shows the shoe sizes from the same class.

Size	Frequency
3	3
4	2
5	4
6	2

Calculate the mean using the table.
Which method was quicker and why?

4 P-S The table shows the heights, h cm, of a class of Year 7 students.

	$135 \leqslant h < 140$	$140 \leqslant h < 145$	$145 \leqslant h < 150$	$150 \leqslant h < 155$	$155 \leqslant h < 160$	Total
Boy	3	7	3	4	0	
Girls	2	2	6	4	1	
Total						

a Copy and complete the table.

b How many girls are shorter than 150 cm?

c How many students are at least 145 cm tall?

d What fraction of students are between 140 cm and 150 cm tall?

5 R A station manager records the number of minutes each train is late by in one hour.

18, 1, 0, 3, 2, 11, 4, 9, 42, 11, 12, 0, 0, 23, 25, 2, 15, 13

a Design a grouped frequency table for the data.
The classes in your table must have equal widths.
Write the inequality for each class.

b Write a sentence about the lateness of the trains.

Investigation

6 The data shows the times, in minutes, that some students spent vigorously exercising in a day.

90   15   10   0   5   0   10   20   25   50   0   0   15
8   50   45   20   30   17   10   30   70   45   25   20

a Make a frequency table for the data. Use 5 equal class intervals.

b Repeat part **a**. This time use 10 equal class intervals.

c Which table do you think shows the data best? Explain your answer.

d Explain your choice of intervals.

7 **R** Here are the results of a Year 7 class's maths test.

12, 13, 14, 12, 12, 19, 20, 23, 24, 18, 3, 19, 20, 29, 30

29, 17, 26, 25, 24, 23, 28, 30, 23, 17, 8, 10, 19, 30, 27, 14

a Calculate the mean, median and mode of the data.

b Which of these measures best represents this data. Why?

c Why is a grouped frequency table better to collect this data than an ungrouped frequency table?

d Complete this frequency table using the data.

Marks (m)	Frequency
$0 \leqslant m < 10$	
$10 \leqslant m < 15$	
$15 \leqslant m < 20$	
$20 \leqslant m < 25$	
$25 \leqslant m \leqslant 30$	

e The same Year 7 class did a second test.
The first test was out of 30, the second test was out of 40.
Explain why using percentage scores is a better method of comparing the class performances in the two tests.

f The table shows the percentage scores for the second test.
Calculate the percentage scores of each student on the first test.
Draw a table using the same class boundaries and complete it for the first test.

Percentage (p)	Frequency
$0 \leqslant p < 10$	2
$10 \leqslant p < 20$	4
$20 \leqslant p < 30$	0
$30 \leqslant p < 40$	0
$40 \leqslant p < 50$	6
$50 \leqslant p < 60$	7
$60 \leqslant p < 70$	1
$70 \leqslant p < 80$	2
$80 \leqslant p < 90$	3
$90 \leqslant p \leqslant 100$	5

g By comparing the two tables, state which test the class did better in. Explain.

h By drawing an appropriate diagram, state which test you think the class did better in. Explain.

Reflect

8 In Q6, you were asked to compare data using tables and using diagrams.

a Which did you find more useful and why?

b Why did you choose the diagram you did to represent the data?

3.3 Stem and leaf diagrams

* Draw stem and leaf diagrams for data
* Interpret stem and leaf diagrams

1 The stem and leaf diagram shows students' results for a Year 9 maths test.

Find:

a the mode

b the range

c the median.

d R Which average can you find most easily from a stem and leaf diagram?

```
0 | 9
1 | 1 3 8
2 | 2 3 5 8 8
3 | 0 1 4 4 6 7 7 7 9
4 | 1 2 2 5 8 9
5 | 0
```

Key: 2 | 5 means 25

2 A group of Year 9 students were tested on their knowledge of countries of the world before and after watching a video.
This back-to-back stem and leaf diagram shows the results.

a Work out the median and range before and after the students watched the video.

b Write two sentences comparing the median and range for before and after.

```
Before video          |   | After video
          8 5 3 2 | 1 | 2
      9 6 6 4 1 0 | 2 | 1 7 9
              2 0 | 3 | 0 6 7 7 8
              8 4 3 | 4 | 2 2 5 9
                    | 5 | 0 0
```

Key   Key
2 | 3 means 32   3 | 6 means 36

3 Here is a list of the scores in a maths test.

12, 13, 14, 17, 19, 12, 14, 16, 20, 22

a Construct a stem and leaf diagram for the data.

b R Why is a stem and leaf data not very useful when interpreting this data?

4 For each stem and leaf diagram, calculate the mean and the median and state which is higher.

a
```
0 | 1 2 2 3 4
1 | 2 2 3 4
2 | 0 1 2 6
3 | 0
4 | 0
```

b
```
1 | 1 2 2 3 4
2 | 2 2 3 4
3 | 0 1 2 6
4 | 0
5 | 0
```

c
```
0 | 1
1 | 0
2 | 0 1 2 6
3 | 2 2 3 4
4 | 1 2 2 3 4
```
Key
1 | 0 means 10

5 P-S Construct a stem and leaf diagram with 15 pieces of data, with a higher mean than median.

6 P-S Construct a stem and leaf diagram with 9 pieces of data, with a higher median than mean.

7 **P-S** Construct a back-to-back stem and leaf diagram where no data items are the same on both sides but where the mean for both sides is the same.

8 **R** The list of numbers shows the ages of some men and women in a club.

Men: 23, 24, 26, 27, 90, 89, 76, 75, 74, 30, 34, 39, 50, 56
Women: 29, 18, 30, 67, 87, 96, 45, 64, 30, 23, 80, 21, 36

a Draw a back-to-back stem and leaf diagram showing the ages.

b Copy and complete the population pyramid to show the women's ages.

> **Q8b hint** A population pyramid is a back-to-back bar chart showing the ages of a population that has a scale of tens.

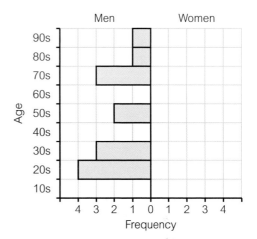

c Which diagram gives you more information? Which would you choose to calculate the mean? Which would you use to find the mode?

d Write three statements comparing the distribution of ages for men and women in the club.

9 This data shows the number of birds that a bird watcher sees each day.

3, 3, 4, 4, 5, 8, 10, 11, 12, 13, 13, 14, 22, 23, 30, 43

a Draw a stem and leaf diagram for this data.

b Copy and complete this grouped frequency table.

Number of birds	Frequency
0–9	
10–19	
20–29	
30–39	
40–49	

Birds seen each day

c Copy and complete this horizontal bar chart.

d **R** What do you notice about the bar chart and the stem and leaf diagram?

Investigation

10 a Draw a back-to-back stem and leaf diagram showing on one side the multiples of 3 between 0 and 100 and on the other side the prime numbers between 0 and 100.

b Between which two numbers are there more prime numbers than multiples of 3?

c What other pieces of information can you see?

Reflect

11 Compare a bar chart and a stem and leaf diagram. Which is better for:

• finding the modal class
• finding the mode
• finding the median
• showing the shape of the data distribution?

3.4 Comparing data

- Compare two sets of data using statistics or the shape of the graph
- Construct line graphs
- Choose the most appropriate average to use

1 **R** The table shows how far, in metres, different remote control toys can go before losing signal.

Q1 hint Which toy was most consistent? Which had the greatest range?

Helicopter	20	20.5	19	21	18	19.5	18
Plane	19	17.5	20	18	18.5	19.5	19.5
Dog	19.5	19	20.5	16	18	20	17.5

Use the ranges and medians to write two sentences comparing the performance of the different toys.

2 Here are the fastest eight women's and men's times for the 5000 m in the 2012 Olympics.

Women   15:04.25, 15:04.73, 15:05.15, 15:05.79, 15:10.66, 15:11.59, 15:12.72, 15:17.88

Men   13:41.66, 13.41.98, 13.42.36, 13:42.99, 13.43.83, 13.45.04, 13.45.30, 13:45.37

a What was the fastest women's time, in minutes and seconds?

b Compare the men's and women's times, using the means and the ranges.

3 The line graph shows the depth of snow at two ski resorts at the end of each month.

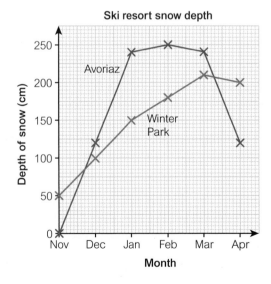

Compare the depths of snow in the two resorts from November to April.

4 **R** The table shows information about the weather in Lerwick, Scotland.

	Jan	Feb	Mar	Apr	May	Jun	Jul	Aug	Sep	Oct	Nov	Dec
Max temp, °C	5	5	6	8	11	13	14	14	13	10	8	6
Rainfall, mm	109	97	69	68	52	55	72	71	87	104	111	118

Copy the axes.

a Draw a bar chart for rainfall (mm).

b On the same graph, draw a line graph for maximum temperature (°C).

c Write two sentences describing how the weather changed during the year.

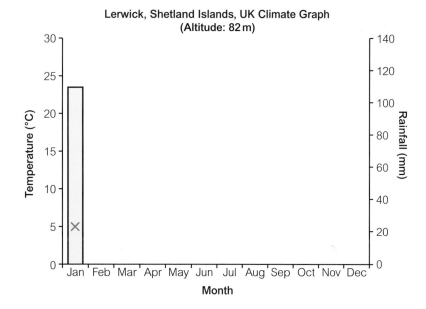

5 **R** The line graph shows the number of full-time and part-time workers in the USA.

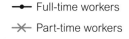
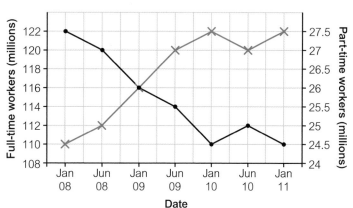

a How many part-time workers were there in June 2010?

b How many full-time workers were there in January 2011?

c A magazine used this caption with the graph:
'Fall in full-time jobs matched by rise in part-time jobs.'
Explain why the caption is wrong.

d Does the point where the graphs cross mean anything?

6 Two students have a mean score of 78 in general knowledge tests.
What other measure do you need, to decide which student would be best to represent the school in a general knowledge quiz? Explain.

3.5 Scatter graphs

- Draw a scatter graph
- Draw a line of best fit on a scatter graph
- Describe types of correlation

1 R This scatter graph shows the
heights of 19 trees in a conservation area,
and the diameter of their trunks 1 m above
the ground.

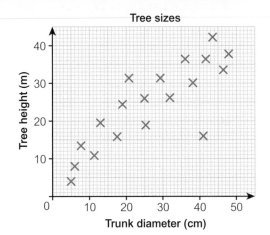

Tree sizes

a Describe the correlation shown by this
scatter graph.

b Write down the height of the tree that had
a trunk diameter of 6 cm.

c Write down the trunk diameters of the trees
that had a height of 26 m.

d Nisha believes that one of the points has
been plotted incorrectly.
Which point do you think this is?
Give a reason for your answer.

e Suggest another reason why one of the data points might not be in line with the others.

2 R This table shows the gestation period and litter size for 8 mammals.

Mammal	Baboon	Dog	Goat	Hamster	Hedgehog	Raccoon	Squirrel	Tiger
Gestation period (days)	180	62	150	16	34	64	38	104
Average litter size	1	4	2	6.3	4.6	3.5	3	3

a Draw a scatter graph to show this information.
Draw a line of best fit on your graph.

b Describe the correlation between gestation period and
litter size. Is the correlation positive or negative?
Is it a strong correlation (all points close to the line of
best fit) or a weak correlation?

Q2 hint The gestation period
for a mammal is the length of
time it takes a foetus to grow
from fertilisation to birth.

c Choose two words from the cloud to complete the sentence below.

shorter
fewer   longer
more

Mammals with _____ gestation periods tend to have _____ offspring in each litter.

3 **R** This table shows the number of plaice recorded at 12 different points in the Barents Sea, and the sea temperature at each point.

Temperature (°C)	1.6	2.4	2.9	0.4	1.2	0.2	1.0	0.6	2.2	2.9	1.7	2.6
Number of plaice	135	70	30	225	145	290	160	250	130	45	100	75

a Draw a scatter graph for this data.

b Describe the correlation between number of fish and sea temperature.

c Draw a line of best fit on your scatter graph.

d Climate scientists estimate that average sea temperatures have increased by approximately 0.2°C.
Use your graph to discuss how this could affect the population of plaice in the Barents Sea.

4 **R** The table shows the price of T-shirts and how many were sold by two different companies.

Price	£12	£15	£20	£25	£30
Designer Tshirts	420	330	510	350	420
TshirtsRus	450	300	120	80	60

a What correlation would you expect to see between the price of a T-shirt and how many were sold?

b Plot the two scatter diagrams and state the type of correlation shown.

5 **R** The table shows the heights of some Y8 students and the lengths of their essays.

Height (cm)	165	157	168	177	173	171	154
Essay length (pages)	1.4	0.7	1.6	2.3	2.1	1.8	0.9

a What correlation would you expect there to be?

b Draw a scatter graph of the data.

c What correlation do you see? Why do you think this is?

Investigation

6 a Measure the length of your thumb and the length of your index finger.
Record this set of data.
Measure this for nine other classmates.
Plot a scatter diagram and draw a line of best fit.

b Describe the correlation between thumb and index finger lengths.

c Does the length of your thumb affect how your index finger grows?
Suggest why the two lengths might be related.

Reflect

7 A study was conducted in the USA that found that there was a strong positive correlation between police numbers and crime rates.
Does this mean that increasing the amount of police will increase the amount of crime? Explain your answer.

3.6 Misleading graphs

- Interpret graphs and charts
- Explain why a graph or chart could be misleading

1 R A laptop manufacturer drew these two line graphs.

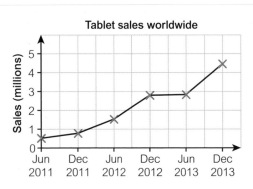

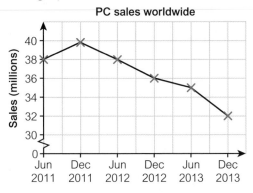

Asha wrote this newspaper headline:

'Massive rise in tablet sales. Epic decline in PC sales.'

a Explain why the line graphs are misleading.

b Draw the PC sales graph using the axis for the tablet sales graph.

c Write a more accurate newspaper headline.

2 R The bar chart shows the downloads of music singles between 2012 and 2018 in the UK.

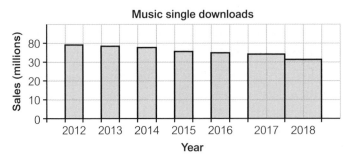

Year	Sales (millions)
2012	78
2013	74
2014	71
2015	56
2016	51
2017	44
2018	31

a Give two reasons why the bar chart is misleading.

b Draw an accurate bar chart.

3 **P-S** The table shows the number of albums sold monthly by two bands.

	Jan	Feb	Mar	Apr	May	Jun	Jul	Aug
The Breakers	1200	1300	1350	1500	1700	1750	1700	1600
Tempest	500	550	500	600	700	850	850	950

a Draw a misleading line graph that suggests The Breakers are improving sales quicker than Tempest.

b Draw a misleading bar chart that suggests that Tempest is improving sales quicker than The Breakers.

Q3 hint You can decide the scale, where the scale starts and how much data to show.

4 **R** To test how a copper tank would expand in high temperatures in a power station, a copper bar 10 m long was heated. Its length was recorded at different temperatures. The results were plotted on this scatter graph.

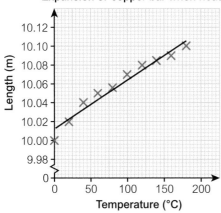

Expansion of copper bar when heated

a Describe the correlation shown by the graph.

b What happens to the length of the copper bar as the temperature increases?

c Why has the 'zigzag' been used, and some values been missed out, on the length axis?

d The graph was plotted to see if there was correlation.
Do the missing values on the length axis affect the conclusion about the correlation?

5 **R** This table shows the age and shell size of eight Dungeness crabs.

Shell size (mm)	152	150	140	133	156	138	142	155
Age (years)	3.3	2.0	2.4	2.3	3.3	2.5	2.7	3.4

a Draw a scatter graph for this data.
Use zigzags on both axes, so there is not wasted space on the graph.

b Describe the correlation between shell size and age.

c Draw a line of best fit on your scatter graph.

Reflect

6 When looking at a graph or chart in the news or on social media, what would you recommend people look out for to avoid being misled?

3 Extend

1 **P-S** Draw a pie chart to represent the following information.

- Dogs like one of five different brands of dog food.
- 50% more dogs liked Flava than liked Lamblicious.
- Lamblicious was liked by 25% of the dogs.
- Dogs liked Bow-wow, FishyMcFish and TunaTreat in the ratio 2 : 2 : 1.

2 **P-S / R**   180 people are asked what type of TV show is their favourite.
Jessie draws a pie chart of the results.
Drama takes up 240° of the pie chart.
The rest of the pie chart is taken up by fantasy, sci-fi, reality and news.
The number of people who chose fantasy is double the number of people who chose sci-fi.
The number of people who chose news is four times the number of people who chose reality.
The number of people who chose reality is one-fifth of the number of people who chose sci-fi.
   a Draw Jessie's pie chart.
   b Draw a bar chart showing this information.
   c Which do you think better shows the data? Why?

3 **R**   A school records the amount of time in minutes Year 11 students spend daily reading books and the grades they achieve in GCSE English.

Time reading (minutes)	5	12	45	3	34	15	18	27
GCSE grade	2	3	6	9	5	4	3	5

   a Which value do you think is an outlier?
   b What kind of diagram do you think is most appropriate to show this data?
   c Draw a scatter diagram to show this data.
   Do you think the school should show this scatter diagram to convince students to read more? Explain your reasoning.

4 **R**   The graph shows the yearly change in the number of flowers grown by Allison and Charlotte.

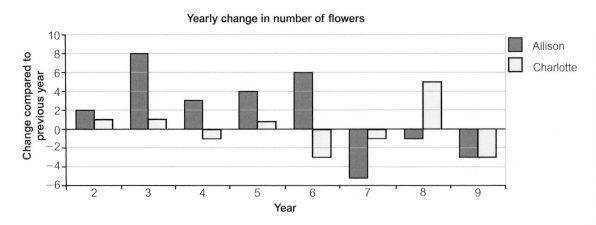

a Who do you think is best at growing flowers?

b In the first year (2010), Allison grew 5 flowers and Charlotte grew 21.
Now who do you think is best? Draw a better graph to display the data.

5 **P-S** Draw a stem and leaf diagram where the range of the data is double the mean and the median is greater than the mean.

6 **R** The mean of the data in a stem and leaf diagram is known.

a One piece of data is missing.
Do you know enough to work out the missing value?

b Two pieces of data are missing.
Do you know enough to work out the missing values?

7 **P-S** The table shows the number of people sitting at tables in a cafe and their frequency.

Number of people	1	2	3	4	5
Frequency	3	x	14	x	15

The mean number of people sitting at a table is 3.6.
Find the missing frequencies.

Investigation

8 Here is a list of the length of some films and the genre of film.

Genre	Length
Fantasy	2 hours 12 minutes
Fantasy	189 minutes
Fantasy	2 hours 14 minutes
Fantasy	1 hour 45 minutes
Super hero	3 hours 15 minutes
Super hero	137 minutes
Super hero	98 minutes
Super hero	125 minutes
Rom-com	89 minutes
Rom-com	78 minutes
Rom-com	2 hours 9 minutes
Rom-com	158 minutes

Using any diagrams and calculations you think are appropriate, compare the length of films between genres.

Reflect

9 During this unit, you have examined many different ways of displaying data.
Give some examples of when you might use each one and why you would choose that diagram.

4 Expressions and equations

Master   **Extend p57**

4.1 Algebraic powers

- Understand and simplify algebraic powers
- Write and use expressions involving powers

1 A sculptor makes two cubes out of concrete. The smaller cube has side length x cm.
The larger cube has a side length 3 times the length of the smaller cube.

 a Write an expression, in terms of x, for the side length of the larger cube.

 b Write an expression for the volume of each cube.

 c Write an expression for the total volume of concrete needed for both cubes. Write your expression in its simplest form.

 d Use your answer to part **c** to work out the total volume of concrete needed for both cubes when $x = 10$ cm.

2 Here is a list of expressions:

$a, a + 2, a - 2, a^2, a^3, 2a, 2a^2, (2a)^2$

 a Write the expressions in ascending order when a is 6.

 b Write the expressions in ascending order when a is $\frac{1}{2}$.

 c R Explain why you do not have enough information to place the expression ab into either of your lists.

3 R Think of a number. Double it. Square your answer.
Divide your answer by 4. Square root your answer.

 a Try this with five numbers. What do you notice?

 b Start with a letter to represent a number. Write an expression for each step.

4 R Imrana says that $(3y)^2$ is always bigger than $3y^2$ if y is a non-zero integer.
Is Imrana correct? Explain.

5 R Hafsa says that if we double x^2, the answer is x^4.
Is this always, sometimes, or never true? Explain your reasoning.

6 P-S A rectangle is made from two identical squares.
Each square has an unknown side length.

 a Write an expression for the area of the rectangle.

 b Write an expression for the perimeter of the rectangle.

 c The rectangle is the cross section of a cuboid.
The cuboid has a depth that is 3 times the length of the square.
Write an expression for the volume of the cuboid.

7 **P-S** The volume of a cuboid can be written as $18x^2$.
One length of the cuboid is 2 cm. The other two lengths are equal.
a Write an expression for this length.
b Sketch a diagram of the cuboid.
c Write an expression for the total of the three lengths of the cuboid.
d Three of these cuboids are stacked together to make a new shape.
Write an expression for the volume of the new shape.

8 **P-S** Lucy is decorating a room. She doesn't know the length of the room, but she does know the length is double the width and the height is the same as the width.
a Write an expression for the total area of the room's walls.
b The floor needs to be tiled.
Write an expression for the area that will need to be tiled.
c 7 tiles will fit exactly down the width of the room.
Each tile has a side length of 30 cm.
Give the dimensions of the room in metres.

9 **P-S / R** A square tile has side length of x cm.
The tiles are placed to make a larger square.
The side of the larger square is made from y tiles.
a Write an expression for the number of tiles needed to make the larger square.
b Write an expression for the total area of the larger square.
c Write an expression for the perimeter of the larger square.
d The larger square is cut in half to form two rectangles, and the two halves are put end to end to make a longer rectangle.
   i Write an expression for the total area of the new rectangle.
   ii Write an expression for the total perimeter of the rectangle.
   iii Given that the tile length is 25 cm, is it possible to decide which has the larger perimeter, the square or the rectangle? Give reasons.

Investigation

10 A lidless cuboid box is made from a sheet of paper measuring 30 cm by 20 cm by cutting squares with side length x cm cut out of the corners.
What integer value of x gives the box with the largest possible capacity?

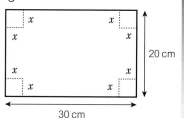

Reflect

11 For each part
   i state whether the pair of expressions are always, sometimes or never equal.
   ii if they are sometimes equal, state the values at which they are equal.
a $2x^2$ and $(2x)^2$ **b** $3x^2$ and $(3x)^2$ **c** $3x^3$ and $(3x)^3$ **d** ab^2 and $(ab)^2$

4.2 Expressions and brackets

- Expand brackets
- Write and simplify algebraic expressions using brackets and division

1 **P-S** A glass holds v millilitres. It is filled with 50 ml of cordial and topped up with water. Jo fills 8 glasses with this drink.

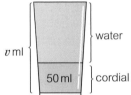

v ml

50 ml

water

cordial

a Write an expression for the amount of water in one glass.

b Write an expression for the amount of water in 8 glasses.

c Jo had a 2-litre bottle of water to make the 8 drinks. Write an expression for the amount of water left in the bottle, in millilitres.

d Expand and simplify your expression from part **c**.

e Calculate the amount of water left in the bottle when $v = 250$ ml.

2 Expand and simplify

    a $3(x + 5) + 4(x - 2)$ **b** $5(m - 4) - 3(m + 1)$ **c** $2(y + 5) - 2(y - 1)$

    d $2(x + 5) - (3x - 2)$ **e** $3(2x + 4) + 2(x - 3)$ **f** $4(3x - 5) - 3(2x - 1)$

3 **a** Write an expression for the area of the larger rectangle.

    b Write an expression for the area of the smaller rectangle.

    c Write an expression for the shaded area.

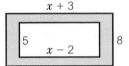

$x + 3$

5    $x - 2$ 8

4 For each shape:

    i write an expression for the area of the shape

    ii expand the brackets in your expression.

a

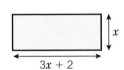

x

$3x + 2$

b

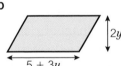

$2y$

$5 + 3y$

c

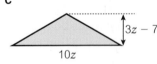

$3z - 7$

$10z$

5 A swimming pool is in the shape of a cuboid that is 25 m long, 10 m wide and 1.6 m deep. The swimming pool is filled with water to an unknown depth.

    a Write an expression for the volume of water in the swimming pool.

    b R Explain why the value of the variable in your expression cannot be 2.

    c The depth of the water in the swimming pool is doubled. Write a new expression, using the same variable as in part **a**.

> **Q5a hint**
> Use a variable to represent the depth of the water.

6 **R** The diagram shows a cuboid.

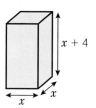

   a Write an expression for the volume of the cuboid.

   b Work out the volume of the cuboid when $x = 5$.

   c Show that an expression for the surface area of the cuboid is $6x^2 + 16x$.

   d Does it matter in which order you multiply the three lengths when calculating the volume?

7 For each shape:

   a write an expression for the perimeter of the shape

   b simplify the expression

   c work out the perimeter when $a = 3$ and $b = -2$.

   A

   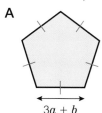

   $3a + b$

   B

   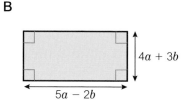

   $4a + 3b$

   $5a - 2b$

   d **R** Is it possible to draw rectangle B with $a = 2$ and $b = -4$? Explain.

8 **P-S** The length of one of the parallel sides of a trapezium is 2 more than the other parallel side.

   The perpendicular height is 5 cm.

   Write an expression for the area of the trapezium.

9 **P-S** This rectangle is made up of six smaller, congruent rectangles.

   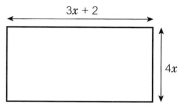

   $3x + 2$

   $4x$

   a Write an expression for the area of the large rectangle.

   b Write an expression for the area of one of the smaller rectangles.

   c What is the area of one of the smaller rectangles when $x = 6$ cm?

   d **R** What can you say about the larger rectangle when $x = 2$ cm?

10 **P-S** The cost of one taxi ride is found by taking the number of miles, adding 20, and then multiplying by the number of minutes the ride takes.

   Write an expression for the cost of a taxi journey.

Reflect

11 Look back at the expressions in Q7.

   a Would it matter if these expressions used the letters x and y instead of a and b?

   b Do the letters help you to understand an expression?

4.3 Factorising expressions

- Factorise expressions

1 Write the highest common factor of each pair.

    a x^2 and x^3 **b** p^2 and p

    c y^5 and y^2 **d** $8z^3$ and $4z$

    e $10m^5$ and $15m^3$ **f** pq and p^2q^2

> **Q1a hint**
> $x^2 = \boxed{x} \times \boxed{x}$
> $x^3 = \boxed{x} \times \boxed{x} \times x$

2 Copy and complete:

    a $\square(x + 3) = 5x^2 + \square$ **b** $3y(\square - 4) = 6y^2 - \square$

3 **P-S** Write three expressions that simplify to $12x(x + 2)$.

4 **P-S** The area of a rectangle is given by the expression $12x^2 + 18$. The sides of the rectangle are integers.

    a Give three possible pairs of expressions for the dimensions of the rectangle.

    b Which pair of expressions represents the full factorisation of $12x^2 + 18$?

    c What is the greatest possible perimeter of the rectangle when $x = 3$?

5 **R** Show which of these expressions can be written as the product of an expression in brackets and one other term.

    $3ab + a$ $3ab + a + b$ $3ab + a + ab^2$ $3ab + a^2b - b^3$

6 **R** The product of two expressions is $5x^3 + 2x$.

    a What are the expressions?

    b Is there more than one answer to part **a**?
       How do you know?

7 **R** Explain why $7x + 5$ cannot be factorised.

8 **R** A rectangle has area $x^2 + 4x$ square metres.
    Show that one of its sides is 4 m longer than the other.

9 **P-S** The solution to each row is found by multiplying the expressions in the row.
    The solution to each column is found by multiplying the expressions in the column.
    Copy and complete the grid, filling in the missing expressions in the grid.

	×		×		$= 5x^2 + 10x$
×					
	×		×		$= 6x^2 - 15x$
=			=		
$10x^3 - 25x^2$			$3x + 6$		

10 P-S / R Ben has an extendable marquee.
The floor area of the marquee is $9x + 3$ square metres.
The length of the marquee can be changed, but the width is always the same.
Both the length and the width are integer numbers of metres.
What are the two possible widths of the marquee?

11 R Show that $8n^2 + 8$ is a multiple of 8 when n is an integer.

12 P-S / R The only common factors of the two terms of an expression are 3, y, 2 and x.
a State the highest common factor (HCF) of the two terms.
b Give three possible original expressions.
c One of the terms is $24x^2y$.
Why can the other term not be $12xy$?

13 P-S / R A rectangle has a length of $x + 4$.
The area of the rectangle is $3x^2 + 12x$.
a Find an expression for the width of the rectangle.
b One side of the rectangle is 3 times the length of the other.
Work out the value of x.

14 The diagram shows a trapezium.

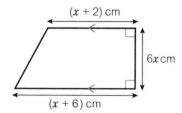

$(x + 2)$ cm

$6x$ cm

$(x + 6)$ cm

Write the area of the trapezium as a fully factorised expression.

15 R Which of these expressions will factorise to give $x(10x - 2)$?

$10x^2 - 2$ $10x^2 - 2x + 5x$ $10x^2 - 2x$ $9x^2 - 2x + x^2$ $9x^2 - x + x^2 - x$

16 R
a Factorise $5x + 5$.
How is this related to 5×11?
b $5(x + 1) = 5 \times 11$
What is the value of x?
c Write 21 as $(x + 1)$.
Use $5(x + 1) = 5x + 5$ to work out the value of 5×21.
d Use a similar factorisation to calculate 13×11.

Reflect

17 Is it possible to use factorisation to check if brackets have been expanded correctly?
Explain your reasoning.

4.4 One-step equations

- Find the inverse of a simple function
- Write and solve one-step equations using function machines

1 **P-S** The length of a rectangle is 3 times its width.

Q1a hint An expression **in terms of** w includes the letter w.

   a Sketch the rectangle. Label its width w.

     What is the length of the rectangle **in terms of** w?

   b The perimeter of the rectangle is 24 cm. Work out the length and the width.

2 In one week, Craig spent 12 hours on his games console. He spent the same length of time each weekday, and twice as much time each day at the weekend.

   a Write an expression using n for the number of hours he spent on his games console in one week.

   b Write and solve an equation to find the value of n.

   c How long did he spend on his games console on Saturday?
     Give your answer in hours and minutes.

3 **P-S** Tickets for 2 adults and 3 children at the zoo come to £28. An adult ticket costs twice as much as a child ticket. Write and solve an equation to work out the price of an adult ticket.

4 **P-S** The probability of Owen watching a reality TV show is 3 times the probability that he watches any other type of TV show.

   a Construct and solve an equation to find the probability of Owen watching a TV show that is not a reality TV show.

   b Owen has seen 20 TV shows this week.
     How many of them would you expect to be reality TV shows?

5 **P-S / R** The perimeter of an equilateral triangle is 15 cm less than the perimeter of a rectangle. One side of the triangle is 3 cm.

   a Construct an equation for the perimeter of the rectangle.

   b What is the perimeter of the rectangle?

   c The rectangle is 3 times as long as it is wide.
     Construct and solve an equation to find the longest side length of the rectangle.

6 For every hour that Cathie works, she gets £9.25.

   a Cathie earned £92.50 in one week.

     i Construct an equation to find out how many hours she worked.

     ii Solve your equation.

   b Cathie works for 12 hours and earns 3 times what Will earns when he works for 10 hours.

     i Construct an equation to find out how much Will gets paid for each hour he works.

     ii Solve your equation.

7 Jamal's wages are calculated using the formula $W = nh$, where n is the number of hours worked and h is the hourly rate.
One month he works 120 hours and earns £1620.
Substitute these values into the formula to give an equation.
Solve the equation to find his hourly rate.

8 The formula for the number of edges of a 3D solid is $E = V + F - 2$, where V is the number of vertices and F is the number of faces.
A 3D solid has 30 edges and 20 vertices. How many faces does it have?

9 **P-S** Each achievement in a video game is worth 50 points.
Lily has 5 times as many points as Hamzah.
Hamzah has completed 12 achievements in the game.
   a Construct an equation to find out how many points Lily has.
   b How many points does Lily have?

10 Work out the missing measurement for each triangle.

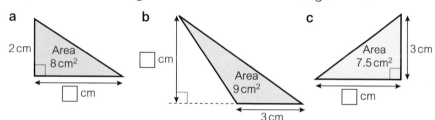

> **Q10 hint** Substitute the values you know into the formula
> Area $= \frac{1}{2}bh$
> then solve the equation.

11 **P-S** A playlist has 378 songs on it.
There are 5 times as many punk rock songs on the playlist than any other type of music.
   a Write an equation to find how many punk rock songs are on the playlist.
   b How many punk rock songs are there on the playlist?
   c Another playlist has the same ratio of punk rock to other types of music.
There are 60 punk rock songs on this playlist.
Construct an equation to find out how many other songs are on the playlist.
   d How many songs are there in total on this second playlist?
   e A third playlist has 252 songs on it. 205 of them are punk rock songs.
Set up and solve an equation to find out if the ratio of punk rock songs to other songs is the same on this playlist.

Investigation

12 Joe is currently 3 times as old as his sister, Francesca.
Francesca was born when their father was 26.
When Francesca's age is half of Joe's, their father will be 30.
Write and solve equations to find out how old their father was when Joe was born.
Write your own version of this using another family.

Reflect

13 Look back at the equations and formulae you have used in this lesson.
What are the differences between an equation and a formula?

4.5 Two-step equations

- Solve two-step equations using function machines
- Solve problems using equations

1 Solve these equations:

a $2x + 11 = 19$ **b** $3x - 2 = 10$

c $8 + 4x = 16$ **d** $12 + 2x = 24$

e $2(x - 1) = 8$ **f** $2x + 8 = 9$

g $4(x - 2) = 2$ **h** $2(10x + 3) - 4x = 2$

2 Solve

a $-3x + 5 = -7$

b $8 - x = -2$

c $5(3 - 2x) - 5x = 45$

> **Q2b hint** Addition can be done in any order. You could rewrite this as $-x + 8 = -2$

3 Solve these equations.
Give your answer as a fraction where necessary.

a $7x + 10 = 5$

b $7x + 10 = 3$

c $-7x + 10 = 5$

4 Solve each equation.
Substitute your answer into the equation to check that you are correct.

a $3(x + 2) = 0$ **b** $3x + 6 = 0$

c $3\left(\frac{x}{3} + 2\right) = 0$ **d** $3\left(x + \frac{2}{3}\right) = 0$

e $3x - \frac{2}{3} = 0$ **f** $3x + \frac{2}{3} = 0$

5 **P-S** Theatre tickets for 2 adults and 1 senior citizen cost a total of £31.
A senior citizen ticket is £5 less than an adult ticket.

a Write an equation for the cost of the tickets.

b Work out the cost of an adult ticket.

6 **P-S** A rectangular piece of card measuring 4 cm by $(x + 5)$ cm has a rectangular hole cut out of it.
The hole measures 2 cm by $(x + 3)$ cm.
The area of card left over is 24 cm².

a Work out the value of x.

b Work out the dimensions of the original piece of card and the hole.

> **Q6 hint** Draw a diagram.

7 James has designed a spinner that lands on the numbers from 1 to 4 according to this table.

Number	1	2	3	4
Probability	x	$2x$	$x + 0.1$	$x + 0.3$

   a R Without any calculations, state which number is least likely.

   b Find the value of x and check your answer to part **a**.

8 P-S / R Consecutive numbers are one after the other, for example 14, 15, 16.
Three consecutive numbers are added together.
The answer is 591.

   a Use trial and error to find the three numbers.

   b Use $n - 1$, n and $n + 1$ to represent the three consecutive numbers.
Write and solve an equation to find n.

   c Write down the three numbers.

   d Which method was more efficient:
writing and solving an equation, or using trial and error?

> **Q8a hint** Try sets of three consecutive numbers, until you find the three that add up to 591.

9 P-S Halle is on holiday in a country where she doesn't speak the language.
She buys lunch for herself and her mum.
They both get the same sandwiches and bottles of orange juice.
There is a sign saying the orange juices cost €0.50 each.
There is no price listed for the sandwiches.
Halle pays with a €10 note and gets €2.70 in change.

   a Write an equation showing this.

   b Solve the equation to calculate how much a sandwich costs.

   c Halle discovers she has misread the sign and the orange juices actually cost €1.50 each.
How much were the sandwiches really?

Investigation

10 The solution to an equation is $x = \frac{3}{7}$.
What could the equation have been?

Reflect

11 Are the solutions to equations always integers?
Are solutions always positive?
Show examples from this lesson to explain.

4.6 The balancing method

> • Solve equations using the balancing method

1 a Write an equation for:

Start with n and multiply by 2. Then add 9. The answer is 25.

Solve your equation to find n.

b Write an equation for:

Start with n and add 9. Then multiply by 2. The answer is 25.

Solve your equation to find n.

c R Both parts **a** and **b** involve multiplying by 2 and adding 9.

Which inverse operations did you use to solve both equations?

What was the same and what was different in the way that you solved them?

2 P-S / R The diagram shows a cuboid and a cube. The volume of the cuboid is greater than the volume of the cube.

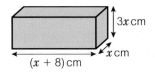

a Write an expression, in its simplest form, for the difference between the volume of the cuboid and cube.

b Use your expression to calculate this difference when

   i $x = 1$ **ii** $x = 2$ **iii** $x = 3$ **iv** $x = 4$

c Explain why it is not possible for x to be an integer greater than 4.

3 Substitute the values given into each formula. Solve the equation to find the unknown value.

a $P = 2v + r$ Work out v when $r = 6$ and $P = 28$.

b $y = mx + c$ Work out x when $y = 11$, $m = 3$ and $c = -1$.

c $D = \frac{w}{8} + v$ Work out w when $v = 5$ and $D = 15$.

d $A = \frac{(a + b)h}{2}$ Work out h when $a = 3$, $b = 4$ and $A = 10.5$.

e $v = u + at$ Work out a when $u = 0$, $t = 10$ and $v = 45$.

f $s = ut + \frac{1}{2}at^2$ Work out u when $t = 2$, $a = 10$ and $s = 30$.

4 P-S The cost of a taxi journey is calculated using $C = \dfrac{t(3m + 0.5)}{4}$, where t is the length of the journey in minutes and m is the number of miles the journey covers.

a Calculate the cost of a journey that lasts for 10 minutes and covers 3 miles.

b The cost of one 5-mile journey is £6.50. How many minutes does the journey last for?

c A journey takes 12 minutes and costs £3.75. How many miles is the journey?

d Dave takes a taxi ride and is charged £10.00.

Dave thinks the journey took 16 minutes to cover 2 miles.

   i How much should Dave have been charged if he was right?

  ii If Dave was only correct about the time, how many miles was the journey?

 iii If Dave was only correct about the distance, how long did the journey take?

5 **P-S** Polly works as a shop assistant.

A customer buys three T-shirts and two pairs of identical trousers for £46 in total.

They know the T-shirts cost £5 each.

They received a 10% discount on their total purchase.

They want to return one of the pairs of trousers.

Write and solve an equation so that Polly knows how much money to give the customer for the returned trousers.

6 **P-S / R** Hugo is buying cat food for his cats, Mog and Zola.

Mog eats three times as much as Zola.

The cats are fed twice a day.

Zola will be at the vets for two days this week so will not need food on those days.

Hugo already has 280 g of cat food.

In order to have the correct amount of food for seven days, Hugo buys 500 g more food.

How much food do Mog and Zola get in one meal?

7 **P-S / R** Marianne makes bracelets.

For every three red beads she uses, she uses two black beads.

Black beads cost £0.30 for 10.

a Marianne is making a bracelet that uses 20 black beads. It costs her £1.80.

Form and solve an equation to work out the cost of one red bead.

b Marianne makes a bracelet that uses 100 beads.

How much will it cost her to make?

c Marianne sells the bracelets for £5 more than it costs her to make them.

Marianne sold a bracelet for £5.54.

How many black and red beads did she use?

8 **P-S / R** Jack goes to the shop and buys 3 apples and 6 pencils to share equally with his two friends.

The pencils cost 30p each.

Jack pays with a £10 note and gets £6.70 in change.

Write and solve an equation to find out the cost of one apple.

9 **P-S** The area of the trapezium is 16 cm².

Write and solve an equation to find the value of x.

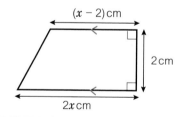

$(x - 2)$ cm

2 cm

$2x$ cm

Investigation

10 Given that $\dfrac{3x + 6}{5} = 12$, you also know that $3x + 6 = 60$ and that $6x + 12 = 120$.

What other facts can you write from the same starting point?

Reflect

11 Which inverse operations will you use, in which order, to solve:

$3x - 7 = 12$ and $3(x - 7) = 12$?

How do you know in which order to use the inverse operations?

4 Extend

1 **R** David is told to think of a number, double it and add four. He is then told to multiply his answer by 5.
How can you use David's answer to tell him his original number?

2 **R** Write and factorise an algebraic expression to show that when 18 is added to any number in the 9 times table, the result is still in the 9 times table.

3 **P-S** The highest common factor (HCF) of the two terms of an expression is $3x$.
The lowest common multiple (LCM) of the two terms is $6x^2$.
What is the expression?

4 **P-S** The angles in a triangle are in the ratio 3 : 4 : 5.
By solving an equation, state whether it is a right-angled triangle or not.

5 **P-S** The perpendicular height of a trapezium is 4 cm.
One of the parallel sides is double the length of the other.
The length of each of the other two sides is 5 less than the length of the shorter of the two parallel sides.
The area of the trapezium is 72 cm^2.
What is the length of each side?

6 **P-S** Copy and complete so that $w = x = y = z = 2$.
$$\square w + \square = x \qquad \square x + \square = y \qquad \square y + \square = z$$

7 **P-S** A shape is made using identical rectangular blocks.
The perimeter of the shape is 56 cm.

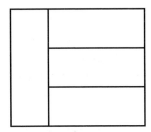

A second shape is made by placing five of the rectangular blocks together so that they are joined by their longest sides.
Calculate the perimeter of the second shape.

8 **P-S** A metal statue with a volume of 8 m^3 is melted down to make seven identical cubes with side length x cm and three cubes with side length 60 cm.
All of the cubes are stacked up on top of each other.
What is the height of this stack?

9 **P-S** Place the expressions
$x - 4, x - 3, x - 2, x - 1, x, x + 1, x + 2, x + 3, x + 4$
into the magic square so that every row and column has the
same sum.
What is the value of x such that the sum of each row and
column is 12?

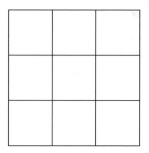

10 **P-S** Three identical cubes are stacked in a tower.
The height of the tower is 27 cm.
Work out the total volume of the tower.

11 **P-S / R**

$$\frac{5}{x} + \frac{5}{8} = \frac{35}{24}$$

Calculate the value of x.

12 **P-S** Six cubes are stacked in a triangular arrangement.
The volume of one cube is 64 cm³.
What is the surface area of the stack of cubes?

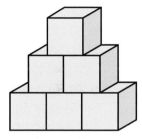

Investigation

13 Replace the letters a, b and c in the equation with integers so that x is also an integer.

$$\frac{ax + b}{3} = c$$

Is it possible for x to be any number from 1 to 10?

Investigation

14 A sequence is produced by adding on a each time, where a is a constant.
Lucy says that the sum of the first three terms will always be a multiple of 3, no matter
what value a has or what the starting number is.
By choosing a value for a, test Lucy's idea.
Show algebraically whether Lucy's idea holds true for any starting value and any value
of a.

Reflect

15 In this unit you have written complicated worded situations algebraically before solving
them. In what ways has this helped you to work through a problem or multiple problems
in the same scenario?

5 Real-life graphs

Master   Extend p71

5.1 Conversion graphs

- Draw, use and interpret conversion graphs

1 The conversion graph can be used to
   convert between centimetres and inches.
   Helena has measured the length of her hair
   and says it is 34 cm long.
   Chelsea has measured her hair and says it
   is 30 inches long.

   a By what percentage is Chelsea's
   hair longer?

   b Helena cuts 10 cm from her hair and
   Chelsea cuts 10 inches from her hair.
   Whose hair is longer now?
   By what percentage?

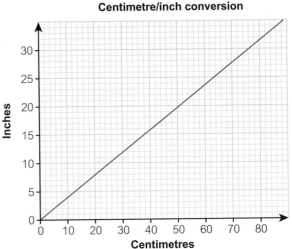

Centimetre/inch conversion

2 The conversion graph shows the conversion between cups and grams for different
   ingredients.

   a Greg is baking a cake.
   The recipe says he needs 2 cups of flour,
   3 cups of sugar and 1.5 cups of butter.
   Greg has 500 g of flour, 500 g of sugar
   and 150 g of butter.
   Does he have enough ingredients?

   b R Julia has a recipe that asks for
   7 cups of sugar.
   Greg says that you can just add the
   amount for 1 cup seven times.
   Is Greg correct? Explain.

   c R Julia is trying to convert a recipe into cups.
   The recipe says she needs 200 g of sugar.
   Julia says this will be 40 000 cups.
   What mistake has Julia made?

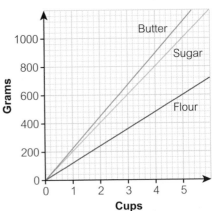

3 **P-S / R** The graph shows the conversion rate between cubic centimetres and litres.

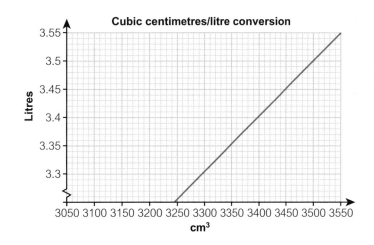

Cubic centimetres/litre conversion

a If the axes were labelled continuously to 0, would the graph go through the origin? How do you know?

b Use the graph to work out whether 7 litres is a greater volume than 702 cm³.

4 **P-S / R** The table shows the conversion between the Kelvin and Celsius units of temperature.

a Draw a conversion graph.

b Why does it not go through the origin?

c At what temperature in Kelvin will water boil?

Celsius	−2	−1	0	1	2
Kelvin	271.15	272.15	273.15	274.15	275.15

5 **P-S** The graph shows the conversion between euros and Norwegian kroner.

a What is the exchange rate from kroner into euros?

b A teddy bear costs 6 euros in Germany or 58 Norwegian kroner in Norway. Where is it more expensive?

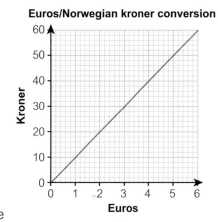

Euros/Norwegian kroner conversion

6 **R** The graph shows a model that a scientist made relating the amount of time university students spend studying the week before an exam and their marks in the final exam.

a Why does the graph not go through the origin?

b Why is the graph not a straight line?

c How many marks would you predict for someone who studied for 1.5 hours?

d The table shows the marks for five students and how many hours they studied.

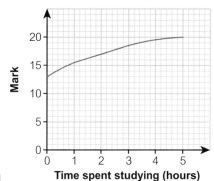

Time spent studying and mark in final exam

Mark	17	18	16	20	19
Time spent studying (hours)	2	3	1	0	5

Compare this to the graph and explain whether you think the model is a good fit.

Reflect

7 Why will a conversion graph for currencies or units of length, mass and volume always be a straight line that passes through the origin?
Are there any conversion graphs that do not?

5.2 Distance–time graphs

- Interpret a distance–time graph
- Draw a simple distance–time graph
- Draw and use graphs to solve distance–time problems

1 Hannah goes on holiday by car.
The distance–time graph shows the five sections of her journey.

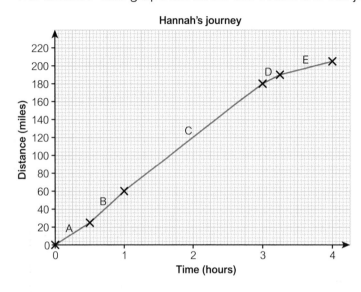

Hannah's journey

Q1 hint In section A of her journey she travels 25 miles in 30 minutes. If she carried on at this speed she would travel 50 miles in 1 hour. So her speed for this section of the journey is 50 miles per hour.

Copy and complete the table.

Section	Distance (miles)	Time taken	Speed (miles per hour)
A	25 − 0 = 25	30 minutes	50
B	60 − 25 = 35		
C			
D			
E	205 −		

2 R Chris jogs 800 m in 15 minutes to his friend's house. He spends 1 hour at his friend's house, then walks home in 30 minutes.

a Sania and Karl sketch graphs to show Chris's journey.

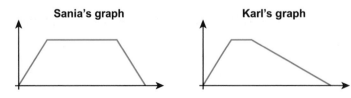

Sania's graph   **Karl's graph**

They are both incorrect. Explain what is wrong with each graph.

b Sketch a more accurate graph for Chris's journey.

3 **R** Michaela is travelling. She records her distance from home at various times.

Time	11 am	12 pm	1 pm	3 pm	4 pm	5 pm
Distance from home (miles)	0	30	70	110	170	200

    a Work out Michaela's speed between 12 pm and 3 pm.

    b Michaela was 110 miles from home at 2 pm.

       Draw a distance–time graph for Michaela's journey.

    c When did Michaela stop for a break?

    d Michaela spent about 1 hour on a motorway. When do you think it was?

    e Why is your answer to part **a** an average speed?

4 **P-S** Athletes A, B and C take part in the London Marathon.

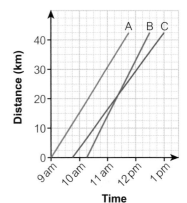

    a How far is the race in kilometres?

    b What time did Athlete C start the race?

    c Which athlete had the fastest time?

    d During the race, Athlete B overtook Athlete C.

      i At what time did this happen?

      ii How far had they each run when this happened?

    e **R** According to this graph, each runner was travelling
at a constant speed. Do you think this is true?

5 **a** Match each race description to a graph.

      i Maddie starts off quickly and then runs
more slowly.

      ii Sophie starts off slowly, then runs faster
towards the finish.

      iii Beckie runs at a constant speed throughout the race.

    b Two other students run in this race.
Here are their graphs.
Write a brief description of their races.

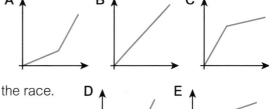

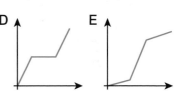

Investigation

6 Draw a sketch of a roller coaster track.

    a What would the distance–time graph of the journey look like?
Use metres for distance and seconds for time.

    b How would your distance–time graph change if the units of the axes changed from
metres and seconds to metres and hours?

    c If the roller coaster does a loop, will the distance–time graph do a loop? Explain.
Try this for different roller coasters.

Reflect

7 In the investigation, you looked at roller coasters and distance–time graphs.

    a What would it mean if a distance–time graph showed a loop?

    b Why are distance–time graphs unlikely to have perfectly vertical sections?

5.3 Line graphs

* Draw and interpret line graphs

1 R In a school science experiment, different masses are added to a spring and the extension is measured. The table shows some of the results.

Mass (g)	300	400	600
Extension (mm)	9	12	18

Q1a hint Plot mass up to 1000 g on the horizontal axis and extension up to 40 mm on the vertical axis. Use sensible scales.

a Plot a line graph for these values.
b Are mass and spring extension in direct proportion?
c Predict how much the spring will extend by with a mass of 350 g.
d Predict how much the spring will extend by with a mass of 1200 g.
A mass of 1000 g is added. The spring extension is 36 mm.
e When this point is added, does the graph still show direct proportion?

2 The table shows the average monthly rainfall and number of rainy days in London.

	Jan	Feb	Mar	Apr	May	Jun	Jul	Aug	Sep	Oct	Nov	Dec
Average monthly rainfall (mm)	52	39	35	43	50	43	41	48	49	71	63	53
Number of rainy days	19	16	16	16	15	13	14	13	15	15	17	17

a Draw a line graph showing the data.
b Rudy wants to visit London for two months.
   Which two months can he expect to have the least rain?
c Arif wants to visit London and experience typical London weather.
   Which month should he visit to see the most typical London weather?

3 R Ursel is looking back over her maths test scores for the year.

Test	Half term 1	Half term 2	Half term 3	Half term 4	Half term 5	Half term 6
Percentage	34%	45%	Missing	54%	63%	72%

a By drawing a graph, help Ursel estimate what percentage she would have got in the test she missed.
b Ursel wants to calculate her average percentage over the year.
   She uses 0 for the missing test. Why is this a problem?
c Why is it not a good idea for Ursel to use these percentages to predict how much she will get in an English test?
d Is it a good idea for Ursel to use these to predict her score in the first maths test of the next school year? Explain your answer.

4 **R** An author has been checking the bestseller position of their book daily and creates a graph to show this.

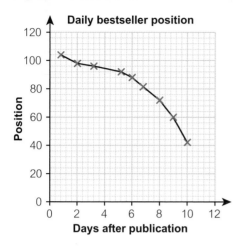

a Estimate the position of their book on the 4th day.

b The author predicts that if the pattern continues, they will be in the top 10 books in two days' time. Do you agree? Refer to the graph in your explanation.

c On the 12th day, the book was at number 44.
   On the 13th day, the book was at number 48.
   How does this change your prediction?

5 **R** The graph shows the speed a car was recorded as driving at every 0.2 hours for a two-hour time period.

a How fast would you predict the car was moving at 1.5 hours?

b How accurate do you think your prediction was?

c A second graph is drawn, using intervals of 1.2 hours. Do you think a prediction from that graph will be as accurate? Explain.

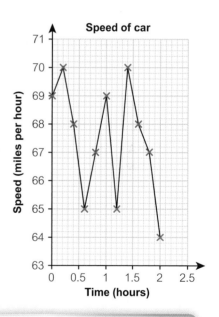

Reflect

6 In Q1 you were asked to plot a line graph.

a Why is your value for 350 g only an estimate?

b Was your estimate for 350 g more or less accurate than your estimate for 1200 g? Explain your reasons.

5.4 More line graphs

- Draw and interpret line graphs and identify trends

1 **P-S** The graph shows the share price of a company in 2013.

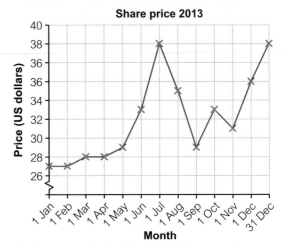

Share price 2013

a Describe the overall trend in the share price during 2013.

b What was the difference in price from the start of 2013 to the end of 2013?

c On what two dates did the price reach a minimum before increasing again?

d On what two dates did the price reach a maximum before decreasing again?

e Ruth bought 160 shares at the beginning of March and sold them at the beginning of November. What was her profit?

f **R** Was the end of 2013 a good time to sell shares in this company?

Q1e hint The profit is the buying price minus the selling price.

2 **P-S** The graph shows the income and expenditure for a town council.

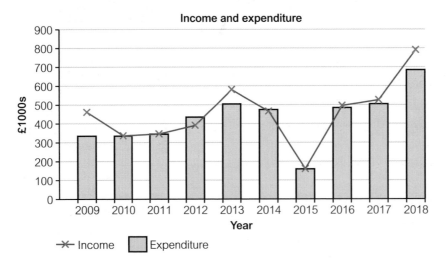

Income and expenditure

—✳— Income   ☐ Expenditure

a What does the value of 200 on the vertical axis represent?

b In 2013, what was the total expenditure of the council?

c In which years was the income over £450 000?

d In which year did the council overspend?

Q2d hint Overspending is when income is less than the amount spent.

e Describe the trend in the income
  i between 2013 and 2015
  ii between 2015 and 2018.

f **R** Is it possible to use the graph to predict the income and expenditure in 2019?

3 **R** The cost of 1 GB of data storage is shown on the graph.

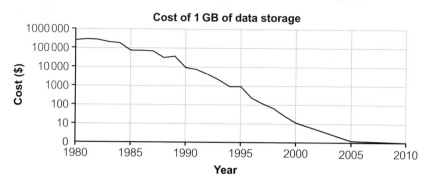

a What is unusual about the vertical scale on the graph? How do you get from one marked value to the next?

b Use the values in the table to draw a graph with a vertical scale of 0, 10000, 20000, …

Q3b hint You could use a graph-plotting package to plot the graph.

Year	1980	1985	1990	1995	2000	2005	2010
Cost ($)	213000	71000	34000	950	26	0.45	0.05

c Describe the trend in the price of data storage between 1980 and 2010.

d Which graph shows the trend more accurately?

Investigation

4 The table shows the number of ice cream sales of two companies over three years.

	2016				2017				2018			
	Q1	Q2	Q3	Q4	Q1	Q2	Q3	Q4	Q1	Q2	Q3	Q4
Ian's Ices	202	251	246	156	168	267	272	133	132	276	289	102
Chloe's Cones	N/A	122	453	32	67	239	393	143	108	216	373	162

Both companies want to make £0.50 of profit from each ice cream they sell.

Georgia wants to invest £600 into one of the ice cream businesses.

By drawing graphs to look at overall trends, help Georgia decide which business to invest in. Estimate how long it will take her to get her £600 back if she keeps 40% of the profits of the business each year.

Hint Q1 stands for **Quarter 1** which is the first three months (or first quarter) of the year: January, February and March. Then **Quarter 2** is April, May and June, and so on.

Reflect

5 Look back at Q1. How is the trend in the first few months different to the trend over the whole time period the graph shows?

5.5 Real-life graphs

- Draw and interpret linear and non-linear graphs from a range of sources

1 Match each description to a line on the graph.

  a The total cost of a phone call for x minutes at 9p per minute.

  b The total cost of a phone call for x minutes at 35p per minute.

  c The total cost of a hotel phone call with a 50p connection fee and 12p per minute.

  d The total cost of a phone call for x minutes at 20p per minute.

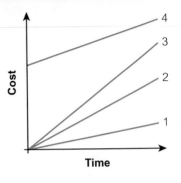

2 Water is poured into these two glasses at the same constant rate.

  a Which fills faster, glass 1 or glass 2?

  b Which graph shows the depth of water in each glass over time?

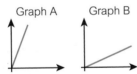

3 The graph shows the percentage of adults in an American town who own a car.

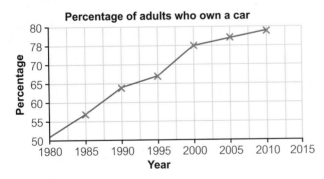

  a What percentage of adults owned a car in 1980?

  b What was the change in percentage of adults owning a car between 1990 and 1995?

  c In which 5-year period did car ownership increase the most?

  d Describe the trend in the percentage of adults who own a car.

  e Use the graph to estimate the percentage of adults who owned a car in 1992.

4 This stacked proportion graph shows the percentages of different age groups in the UK between 1911 and 2011.

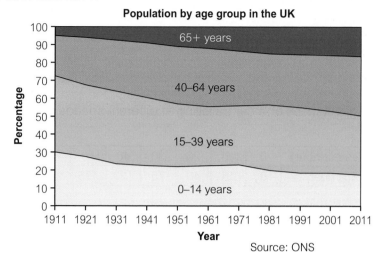

Population by age group in the UK

Source: ONS

a Approximately what percentage of the population was aged 0–14 years in
   i 1911   **ii** 2011?

b Describe the trend in the percentage of the population aged 0–14 years between 1911 and 2011.

c Which age groups have seen a rise in their percentage since 1911?

d R On the whole, is the UK population getting older or younger? Explain your answer.

5 R Sketch a graph to show the electricity use in a school over a 24-hour period. Explain your sketch.

6 The table shows the life expectancy of men and women in Somalia for a 10-year period.

	2007	2008	2009	2010	2011	2012	2013	2014	2015	2016	2017
Female	54.6	54.9	55.3	55.6	56.0	56.3	56.7	57.1	57.6	58.0	58.4
Male	51.5	51.8	52.1	52.4	52.8	53.1	53.5	53.9	54.3	54.7	55.1
Average	53.0	53.3	53.7	54.0	54.3	54.7	55.1	55.5	55.9	56.3	56.7

By drawing graphs, compare the life expectancy of men and women over the 10-year period and describe the overall trend.

7 In Q4 you were asked to describe the trend in the percentage of the population aged 0–14 years.
Do you think this would have been as easy to do if you just had the list of percentages? Explain your answer.

5.6 Curved graphs

- Draw and interpret curved graphs from a range of sources

1 **P-S** The stopping distances of a car travelling at different speeds in dry weather are shown in the table.

Speed of car (miles per hour)	0	10	20	30	40	50	60	70
Stopping distance (feet)	0	15	40	75	120	175	240	315

a Draw a graph to show the data in the table. Plot 'Speed of car (mph)' on the horizontal axis, and 'Stopping distance (ft)' on the vertical axis. Plot your points and join them with a smooth curve.

b Use your graph to estimate the stopping distance of a car travelling at 55 mph.

c A car needs to stop before it hits a wall 20 feet away.
What is the fastest speed it can be travelling at to stop in time?

d What is the difference in the stopping distance of a car travelling at 20 mph and 30 mph?

e **R** Do you think the stopping distances of the car will be the same in all weather conditions?

2 **P-S / R** A BASE jumper jumped off a building 300 m high.
He fell for a certain distance, and then opened his parachute before coming to land.
The graph shows his height above ground during the first 13 seconds of his jump.

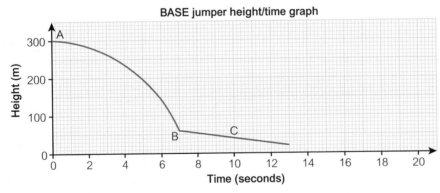

BASE jumper height/time graph

a Match points A, B and C to these statements.
  i Descending with parachute open
  ii Jumping off building 300 m high
  iii Opening parachute

b At what height did the BASE jumper open his parachute?
Explain how you can tell this from the graph.

c How many seconds does it take the BASE jumper to descend 20 m once he has opened his parachute? Explain your answer.

d How many seconds after he jumped do you think he will land? Explain your answer.

3 **R** These 4 containers are filled with water.

a Match each graph to a container.

b One container does not have a graph.
Sketch a graph for that container.

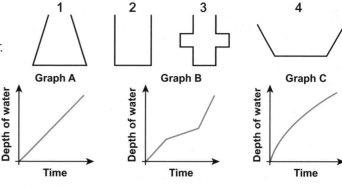

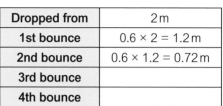

4 **P-S** When a basketball bounces, it goes back up to about 60% of the height it was dropped from.
A basketball is dropped from a height of 2 m.

a Copy and complete this table showing the height of a basketball after four bounces. Round each answer to the nearest centimetre.

Dropped from	2 m
1st bounce	0.6 × 2 = 1.2 m
2nd bounce	0.6 × 1.2 = 0.72 m
3rd bounce	
4th bounce	

A power-ball is dropped from a height of 10 m. The graph shows the height of the ball after two bounces.

b Copy and complete this table showing the height of a power-ball after four bounces.

Number of bounces	0	1	2	3	4
Height (m)					

Q4b hint Use the graph to complete the table for 0, 1 and 2 bounces. Then use these heights to work out the percentage that the power-ball bounces back each time.

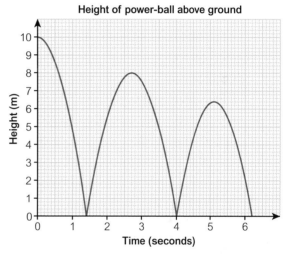

Height of power-ball above ground

5 **P-S / R** Luke throws a ball straight up into the air.
The table shows the ball's height above the ground.

Time (s)	0	1	2	3	4	5	6	7	8
Height (m)	1	38.1	65.4	82.9	90.6	88.6	76.6	54.9	23.4

a Draw a graph to show this information.

b Is the ball travelling at a constant speed? How can you tell?

c Why does the height not start at 0?

d Estimate the times when the height of the ball is 50 m.

e Why are there two times when the ball is at 50 m?

f Use the graph to estimate the time when the ball will hit the ground if Luke doesn't catch it.

Q5a hint
Put Time on the horizontal axis and Height on the vertical axis.
Plot the points and join them with a smooth curve.

Reflect

6 Look back at your answers to Q3.

a Explain why Graph C is a curve and not a straight line.

b How is this similar to the graph for an object thrown in the air? How is it different?

5 Extend

1 **R** A scientist does an experiment to measure the different pressures created by the same force. She does this by changing the area over which the force is applied.
The graph shows her results.

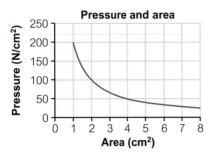

a Copy and complete:

As the area increases, the pressure _____.

b What is the pressure when the same force is applied over an area of 3 cm²?

c Will the pressure ever reach zero?

d Explain why the graph will never meet the vertical axis.

e Use these results to explain why

   i people in high-heeled shoes should not walk on the gym floor

   ii a sharp knife will cut vegetables more easily than a blunt knife

   iii ballet dancers get problems with their toes.

2 A scientist recorded the number of bacteria in a sample.

Time (hours)	0	1	2	3	4	5
Number of bacteria	1	2	4	8	16	32

a How many bacteria would you expect there to be after 6 hours?

b Draw a pair of axes with Time from 0 to 10 on the horizontal axis and Number of bacteria from 0 to 1100 on the vertical axis.

c Plot the points on the axes and join them with a smooth curve.

d Continue the curve up to 10 hours.

e Use your graph to estimate how many bacteria there will be after

> **Q2d hint** Extend the table of values up to 10 hours.

   i $6\frac{1}{2}$ hours

   ii $8\frac{1}{2}$ hours.

3 **P-S** For each vase, sketch a graph showing the depth of water in the vase as it fills with water.

a   **b**   **c**    **d**

4 P-S / R Charles has plotted the length of time he boils his egg for against how perfect the egg was (according to his 5-point egg perfection scale). The graph shows this relationship.

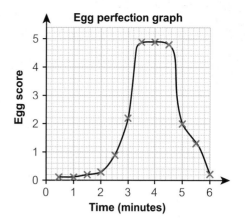

Egg perfection graph

 a Estimate how many minutes Charles should boil an egg for to get a perfect 5/5 egg.
 b Why is this point not shown on the graph?
 c Why are there no negative points on the graph?
 d Why would you expect the graph to be this shape?

5 P-S / R The graph shows the **count rate** against time for chromium-51, which is a radioactive material.

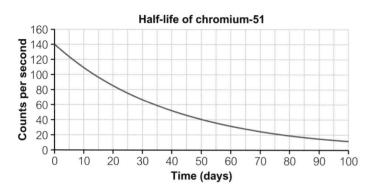

Half-life of chromium-51

> **Q5 hint** The **count rate** is the number of radioactive emissions per second.

 a What is the count rate after 25 days?
 b After how many days does the count rate reach 50?

The half-life of a radioactive material is the time it takes for the count rate to halve.

 c What is the half-life of chromium-51?
 d Does the count rate ever reach zero?

Investigation

6 Sally estimates that the value of a car decreases by 10% every year.
Sally's family buys a new car in 2015 for £15000.
In 2018, they buy a second car for £8000.

 a Plot a graph of the values of the two cars over time.
 b Use the graph to compare the values of the two cars.
   Will the second car ever be worth more than the first?
 c Will either of the two cars ever be worth £0, according to this model?
 d What problems does this model have?

Reflect

7 What information is easier to see from a graph?
What information is easier to work out from a table?

6 Decimals and ratio

Master   Extend p81

6.1 Ordering decimals and rounding

- Round decimals to 2 or 3 decimal places
- Round numbers to a given number of significant figures
- Round numbers to an appropriate degree of accuracy
- Order decimals of any size including negative and positive decimals

1 **R** The tables show the drainage areas (in km²) of 10 river basins.

River basin	Drainage area (km²)
Nile	3 254 555
Amazon	6 144 727
Yangtze	1 722 155
Mississippi	3 202 230
Yenisei	2 554 482

River basin	Drainage area (km²)
Yellow River	945 000
Ob	2 970 000
Paraná	2 582 672
Congo	3 730 000
Amur	1 929 981

   a Write each area in millions to 1 decimal place.

   b Round each area in millions to 1 significant figure.

   c Which rounding is more accurate: rounding to 1 decimal place or to 1 significant figure?

   d Do you think the areas in the table are rounded values? Explain.

2 Here is a list of decimals: 0.345, 0.354, 0.3504, 0.3405

   a Write the decimals in ascending order.

   b **R** Write each decimal correct to 2 decimal places.
     Is it still possible to accurately order them? Explain.

   c Write each decimal correct to 1 decimal place.
     Were you able to use your answers to part **b** to do this?

3 **P-S** Write down a number with 3 decimal places that would round to:

   a 3 to the nearest whole number and 3.2 to the nearest tenth

   b 3 to the nearest whole number and 2.5 to the nearest tenth

   c 2 to the nearest whole number and 2.5 to the nearest tenth

   d 3.2 to the nearest tenth and 3.25 to the nearest hundredth

   e 3.3 to the nearest tenth and 3.25 to the nearest hundredth.

4 **R** A room is measured as 3.57 m by 2.55 m.

   a Calculate the area and perimeter of the room.

   b Round each original measurement to 1 significant figure.

   c Calculate the area and perimeter of the room using the rounded values.

   d Is your answer to part **c** an overestimate or an underestimate? Why?

   e A different room is measured as 3.47 m by 2.45 m.
     Complete parts **a**–**d** again for this room. What is the same and what is different?

5 There are 2.75 million people in a city.

  a Write the number of people correct to 2 significant figures.

  b 192 375 more people arrive in the city over two years.

   i How many million people live in the city now?
   Give your answer correct to 2 significant figures.

   ii How many million people arrived in the city?
   Give your answer correct to 2 significant figures.

   iii By rounding the values to 1 significant figure, write an estimate for the number of new arrivals as a proportion of the original number of people in the city.
   Give your answer as a fraction in its simplest form.

6 **R** 'Truncation' means to shorten a number by cutting off any digits beyond a certain point.

  a A length was measured as 3.75 cm. Georgina truncated it to 3 cm, but Barry rounded it to 4 cm. Who was closer to the original number?

  b Lena has truncated a number to 7. Georgina has rounded it to 8.
  What could the number have been?

7 **P-S / R** At the end of each week, Hafsa works out how much money to put into her savings account.
She rounds her spending to the nearest £10. If an amount rounds up, then she puts the difference between the real amount and the rounded value into her savings account.

  a Hafsa spends £145.89 a week on rent. How much money does she put into her savings from rounding up her rent in a year?

  b Hafsa spends £47 a week on groceries. What is the mean amount that she puts into savings each month from rounding her spending on groceries?

  c Hafsa spends £23 a month on travel expenses. Why does she not put extra money into her savings from that?

  d In July, Hafsa spent a total of £342 on paying bills. Is it possible to work out how much money Hafsa put into savings in July from rounding her spending on bills? Explain.

  e Hafsa's friend suggests that she rounds everything to 1 significant figure instead.
  Given Hafsa's expenses, do you agree with this idea?

8 **P-S / R** A hot chocolate jar says that it has 30 servings in it.
It says that each serving is 5 g and there are 150 g in a packet.
Lee used a teaspoon to measure out his hot chocolate. He only got 28 servings from the jar.

  a Does Lee's teaspoon hold more or less than 5 g of hot chocolate?

  b Lee weighed how much powder he was using and found he was using 5.6 g.
  In the next jar of hot chocolate he bought, he got 25 servings with half a serving left over.
  By rounding, find out if there could have been the correct amount of hot chocolate powder in the jar.

Reflect

9 **a** Give an example where it is not useful to round a number or value.

  b Give an example where it is useful to round a number or value.

  c Does it matter if you round using decimal places or significant figures? Explain.

> **Hint** Look back at some of the questions you have answered to help you.

6.2 Place-value calculations

- Multiply any number by 0.1 and 0.01
- Multiply larger numbers
- Multiply decimals with up to and including 2 decimal places

1 Here is a multiplication fact:
$$6.7 \times 82 = 549.4$$
Use the multiplication fact to work out the answers to each calculation.
  a 6.7×8200 **b** 6.7×0.82 **c** $549.4 \div 6.7$

2 The number 0.0062 can be written as 6.2×0.001.
0.00062 can be written as 6.2×0.0001.
  a Write 0.000062 as the product of 6.2 and another number.
  b Write 0.00000358 as the product of 3.58 and another number.
  c Write 0.00000000098 in the same format.

3 **a** Work out 30% of 450.
  b Multiply 450 by 0.3.
     Compare this with your answer to part **a**.
     What do you notice?
  c Write an equivalent decimal calculation for 35% of 450.

4 **P-S** Alissa has accidentally multiplied by 70 instead of 0.7.
What number can she multiply her current answer by to get the correct answer?

5 **R** Why does multiplying by a decimal that is smaller than 1 give an answer that is smaller than the original number?

6 Work out
  a $(198 + 1980) \div 198$ **b** $(342 + 3420) \div 3.42$
  c $(198 + 1980) \div 1.98$ **d** $(432 + 432000) \div 432$
  e Write two more calculations that use the same idea.

7 **P-S** Create a multiplication grid using the digits 1, 2, 3, 4 once and only once each and as many of the digit 0 as you want.
Do not use any integers.
A must be larger than B, but smaller than C.
D must be smaller than the sum of B and C.

×	?	?
?	A	B
?	C	D

8 **P-S** The product of two positive numbers is smaller than either of the two original numbers.
The sum of the two numbers is 1.2.
What could the two numbers be?

9 R

    a Work out $98 \div 4$.

    b Use your answer to part **a** to decide if 4 is a factor of 980. Explain.

    c Is 4 a factor of 1180? Explain.

    d Is 8 a factor of 1460? Explain.

hint box:

> **Q9 hint** Use the method from parts **a** and **b** to answer parts **c** and **d**.

10 Find the missing digits, A, B and C, in this calculation.

```
  A 2.4
×   B.C
───────
102.9 2
```

11 P-S / R   A number H.G has its digits reversed to G.H.
These two decimal numbers are multiplied together.

    a How many decimal places would you expect the answer to have?

    b H is 2 more than G and G is not 0.
       Give two possible calculations and their answers.

    c The answer to H.G × G.H rounds to 80 to the nearest 10.
       What are G and H?

12 P-S / R   The number line shows the numbers A, B and C.
B is approximately one-quarter of the way between A and C.

```
3                 A   B           C       4
└────────────────┴───┴───────────┴───────┘
```

A is half the sum of B and C, multiplied by 0.9.
What could A and C be?

Investigation

13 Binary is a place-value system where the place-value columns represent powers of 2.
2 is written as 10 in binary: one 2 and zero 1s.
3 is written as 11: one 2 and one 1.
4 is written as 100: one 4, and zero 2s and 1s.

    a Try to write the numbers from 1 to 10 in binary.

    b A binary calculation is 100 × 101 = 10100
       What is the calculation in decimal (base 10) numbers?

    c What other calculations can you write from this?
       Use the techniques you have explored in this lesson to help you.
       Check your answers in decimal notation.

Reflect

14 Describe the steps you took to answer Q1c. Try to use mathematical language in your description, for example 'inverse' and 'place value'.

Unit 6 Decimals and ratio   **76**

6.3 Calculations with decimals

- Divide by 0.1 and 0.01
- Multiply and divide by decimals
- Solve problems involving decimals and all four operations

1 **P-S / R** Here is an incomplete multiplication grid:

×			1.001
	0.007		7.007
6		1.2	
0.001	0.000 001		
8.09		1.618	
		1.816	9.089 08

Copy and complete the grid.

2 Use mental and written methods to work out:

   a $0.4^2 \times (1 - 0.8)$ **b** $0.2 \times 3.5 + 0.3^2$

   c $0.4^3 + \sqrt{0.16} + 1.1^2$ **d** $(2.8 + 3.2)^2 + (0.75 - 0.250)^2$

3 **P-S** A football pitch can be any length between 90 m and 120 m, and any width between 45 m and 90 m to the nearest metre. What is the minimum area of a football pitch?

4 **P-S** Ramiz is thinking of assembling a bike from spare parts bought online. The prices of the main items are given in these tables.

Part	Price
frame	£495.00
wheels (each)	£112.49
gears	£37.99
brakes (each)	£53.75
saddle	£20.99

Part	Price
seat pillar	£47.36
handlebars	£39.96
tyres (each)	£43.75
chain	£11.89
inner tubes (each)	£4.49

   a How much would making such a bike cost?

Postage and packing adds 10% to the price.

   b How much will it cost to have all the components delivered?

A similar new bike in a local bike shop costs £1150.

   c Which would be cheaper, and by how much?

5 The length of the coastline of the UK is around 12.5 thousand km.
Rewrite each coastline length as a multiple of the length of the UK coastline correct to 2 decimal places.

Country	Coastline length (thousands of km)
USA	19.924
Greenland	44.087
Australia	25.76
France	3.4

6 **P-S / R** A trapezium has parallel sides.
One parallel side of the trapezium is 0.9 cm longer than the length of this rectangle.

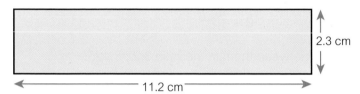

2.3 cm

11.2 cm

The height of the trapezium is 3.2 cm.
The rectangle and the trapezium have the same area.
Calculate the length of the other parallel side of the trapezium.

7 **P-S / R** The height of a triangle is an integer.
The triangle has 1.1 times the area as the rectangle in Q6.
What could the possible height and base lengths of the triangle be?

8 **P-S / R** A metal cube has a side length of 0.4 cm.
It is melted down and made into eight identical smaller cubes.
a What is the side length of each of the smaller cubes?
b Three of the smaller cubes are melted down to make a cuboid that has a rectangular face that measures 0.2 cm by 3 mm. What is the depth of the cuboid?

Investigation

9 Think of a number between 0 and 1.
Multiply it by 3.
Subtract 0.1.
Add 0.4.
Double it.
Subtract 0.6.
Divide by 6.
Do you always end up at your original number? Explain.

Reflect

10 How do you use your knowledge of multiplying and dividing by powers of 10 when multiplying and dividing decimals? Give examples.

Extend p81

6.4 Ratio and proportion with decimals

- Divide a quantity into three or more parts in a given ratio
- Use ratios involving decimals
- Solve ratio and proportion problems
- Use unit ratios

1 Write these ratios in their simplest form.

a $1 : 2.5$ **b** $1 : 3\frac{1}{4}$ **c** $2 : 3.5$ **d** $5 : 1\frac{1}{10}$

e $1 : \frac{5}{3}$ **f** $\frac{3}{5} : \frac{5}{3}$ **g** $0.7 : \frac{7}{6}$

2 Barry and Adam have £999 to share between them in the ratio $3.2 : 5.125$.
  a Use the ratio to work out how much Barry and Adam each get.
  b Write the ratio in its simplest form (without using decimals).
  c Use the simplest form of the ratio to recalculate how much Barry and Adam should each get.
  d R Which form of the ratio did you prefer to use and why?

3 P-S Each month, Sophia spends $\frac{2}{5}$ of her pocket money on food and $\frac{1}{4}$ on comics.
  She saves the rest.
  Write the ratio of her spending, on food to comics to saving, as a ratio in its simplest form.

4 P-S / R
  a On a particular day, the ratio of pounds to euros is £200 : €229.
    i What is the ratio of £1 : €?
    ii What is the ratio of €1 : £?
    iii Which ratio is more useful if you are travelling from the UK to France?

  b On another day, the ratio of pounds to dollars is £50 : $79.
    i What is the ratio of £1 : $?
    ii What is the ratio of $1 : £?
    iii Which ratio is more useful if you want to open a shop in the USA?

5 P-S The sides of a triangle are in the ratio $2 : 3 : 7$. The shortest side is 8 cm.
  Calculate the perimeter of the triangle.

6 Write these ratios in the form $1 : n$.
  a 50 cm : 2 m   **b** 200 m : 1.2 km   **c** 6 hours : 1 day

7 Write these ratios in the form $n : 1$.
  a 6 m : 800 cm   **b** 43 cm : 10 mm

> **Q7a hint** Remember to convert to the same units first.

8 **R** A shop has two different offers on paper plates.

OFFER A
6 paper plates for 90p

OFFER B
4 paper plates for 72p

   a Write the ratio of number of paper plates to price, in its simplest form, for Offer A and Offer B.

   b Which gives better value for money?

   c Write a sentence stating why it is useful to represent ratios in the form $1 : n$.

9 **P-S** Dylan made an orange drink using orange squash to water in the ratio 2 : 9.
Sarah made another drink using orange squash to water in the ratio 3 : 10.

   a Write each of these ratios in the form $1 : n$.

   b Which drink was stronger?

10 The table gives the mass and radius for each of three planets.

Write the ratio of mass to radius for each planet in the form $1 : n$.

Planet	Mass (septillion kg)	Radius (km)
Earth	5.97	6371
Mars	0.642	3390
Mercury	0.330	2440

11 The bar chart shows the number of visitors to a theme park in June and July.

   a Write the proportion of adults to children each month in the ratio $1 : n$.

   b Which month had the higher proportion of children?

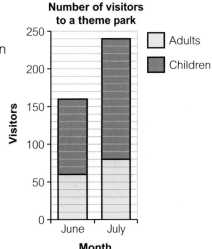

Number of visitors to a theme park

12 **P-S** Some cyclists prefer fixed-wheel bikes, with two cogs and no gears.
Typically a front cog has 50 teeth and a rear cog has 20 teeth.

   a What is the ratio of front cog teeth to rear cog teeth in the ratio $1 : n$?

   b The pedals turn the front cog. How many times does the rear cog turn for every turn of the pedals?

A typical bike travels 195.3 cm for every rotation of the rear wheel.

   c How many times must a cyclist turn the pedals to travel 1 km on a fixed gear bike?

Reflect

13 **a** When is it useful for a ratio to include a decimal? Give examples.

   b When is it useful for a ratio including a decimal to be simplified to give a ratio involving integers? Give examples.

> **Hint** Look back at some of the questions you have answered to help you.

6 Extend

1 **P-S / R** Afrah wants to buy a coat from Japan. It costs ¥7 320.50.
She will have to pay shipping of £25.30.
She has found a company that will charge her £80 for the coat and shipping combined.
The exchange rate is currently £2 : ¥292.82.
Should Afrah use the company or buy the coat and pay for shipping herself?
Give a mathematical explanation.

2 **P-S** Here is a number: 304 050 901 080

    a Split the number above into two parts to make two decimal numbers, keeping the digits in
    the same order they appear in the original number.
    Place a decimal point into each of the parts so there is at least
    one digit after the decimal point.
    Do not include any additional digits.
    Round each of your two numbers to 1 significant figure.
    Multiply your two numbers.
    What is the largest answer you can get?

> **Q2a hint** For example, you could choose 30.40 and 5 090 108.0.

    b Repeat the steps from part **a**, but without rounding.
    How does this change your answer?

3 **P-S / R** Q is multiplied by the decimal $Q.P$ where Q and P are non-zero digits.
Is it possible for the answer to be an integer? If so, what are the values of Q and P?

4 **P-S / R** A number written to 2 decimal places is represented as a.bc
The tenths digit of this number is three times more than the hundredths digit.
The hundredths digit is double the units digit.
The number is multiplied by another number written to 2 decimal places as c.ba.
What is the result of the multiplication?

5 **P-S** Louise reads for 6 hours and 30 minutes during the average week.
Louise reads a 400-page book in 10.4 hours.

    a How long does it take Louise to read one page?
    b Estimate how many pages Louise can read in one minute.
    c Use your estimate to part **b** to estimate how many pages Louise can read in an hour.
    d How many pages would Louise expect to be able to read in an average week?
    e Louise is off school for 6 weeks. She doubles the amount she reads in a week.
    How many 400-page books could Louise read over the school holiday?
    f **R** Half of the books Louise reads are actually 200 pages long.
    How many books will Louise read over the school holiday?

6 **P-S** Bradley thinks of a number, doubles it, adds 3 and then rounds the number to
1 significant figure.
Josh thinks of a different number, follows the same process and gets a smaller answer.
The product of their answers is 600.
What could the original numbers have been?

7   **P-S**   Fill in the blanks to make a ratio that simplifies to 1 : 2.

$\frac{\square.\square}{2} : \frac{3}{5}$

8   **P-S / R**   Pasha and Maria share an amount of money in the ratio 1.3 : 1.4.
Maria gives all of her money to her sons Andrew and Santiago in the ratio 3.3 : 5.8.
Santiago gets £5 more than Andrew.
How much money did Pasha and Maria originally share?

Investigation

9   Using the digits 1, 2, 3, 4, 0, 0, 0, 0 and no others, fill in the blanks to create a set of
three numbers with a mean as close as possible to the median of your sequence.

Investigation

10   The coastline paradox is that the greater the accuracy level used, the larger the
coastline is.

Measure the length of your arm using a metre stick.
Now measure it using a ruler.
Now use a length of string to measure the length.
What do you notice about your accuracy?
Is there a suitable level of accuracy that you can give your lengths to?

Try this for other lengths in the classroom.

Create a picture that is larger if you measure the perimeter correct to the nearest cm
than if it is measured correct to the nearest metre and larger still if you measure the
perimeter correct to the nearest mm.

Reflect

11   Would you prefer to complete all your work in fractions or in decimals?
Which do you think is more accurate?

7 Lines and angles

Master   Extend p93

7.1 Quadrilaterals

- Classify quadrilaterals by their geometric properties
- Solve geometric problems using side and angle properties of special quadrilaterals

1 R Work out the angles and sides marked with letters.

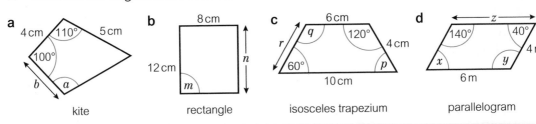

kite   rectangle   isosceles trapezium   parallelogram

Investigation

2 Sketch these quadrilaterals: square, rectangle, parallelogram, rhombus, kite.

a Draw the diagonals.

b Use line and rotational symmetry to mark any equal lengths and angles.

c Copy and complete the table to show the properties of the quadrilaterals.

Quadrilateral	Diagonals bisect each other	Diagonals bisect the interior angles	Diagonals cross at right angles
square			

3 R Work out the angles and sides marked with letters.

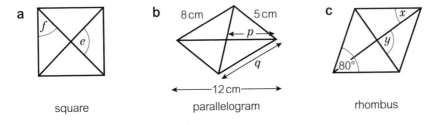

square   parallelogram   rhombus

4 R For each shape:

  i name the shape

  ii work out the angles marked with letters. Give a reason for each answer.

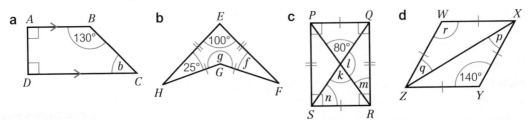

5 **R** A rectangle has opposite sides equal and all angles are 90°.
Which of these shapes is a rectangle?

    parallelogram   square   kite

6 **R** A square is a special type of rectangle.
a Copy and complete this sentence.
A rectangle is a special type of _____.
b Write two more sentences like this about different shapes.

7 **P-S** Draw three different four-sided shapes that contain two or more parallel lines.

8 **P-S** Marcin makes metal wall art by overlapping shapes around a
point. He starts with one rhombus, then overlaps the next one by
dividing the angle at the base in the ratio 2 : 1.
a Work out the sizes of angles a and b.
b Show that angle c is 30°.

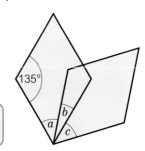

> **Q8b hint**
> c = small angle in rhombus − angle b

Marcin continues the pattern, overlapping each rhombus by the same amount each time.

  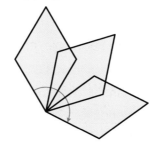

The table shows the total angle used around the centre point each time an extra
rhombus is added.

Number of rhombuses	1	2	3	4	5
Total angle	45°	75°			

c Copy and complete the table.
d What is the term-to-term rule for the 'total angle' sequence of numbers?
e The pattern is complete when the final rhombus overlaps behind the first rhombus.
How many rhombuses will Marcin need to complete the pattern?

9 **P-S** The diagram shows six congruent
trapezia that fit exactly around a point.
Work out the size of angle a. Explain your reasoning.

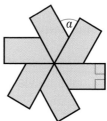

Reflect

10 You know that a shape is a kite.
How does this help you to work out missing sides and angles?

7.2 Alternate angles and proof

- Identify alternate angles on a diagram
- Understand proofs of angle facts

1 Work out the size of angle x for each shape.

a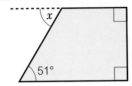

b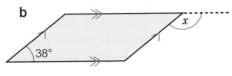

2 **R** The diagram shows a three-stage ramp into a car park.

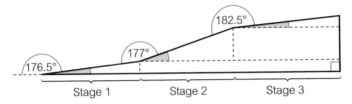

Recommendations for a three-stage ramp are:

- stages 1 and 3 have an angle of less than 3.6° with the horizontal
- stage 2 has an angle of less than 7.1° with the horizontal.

Does this ramp meet the recommendations?
Explain your answer.

3 **P-S / R** A student believes the walls in their maths classroom are not parallel.
They measure the angle a stripe on the carpet makes with each wall.

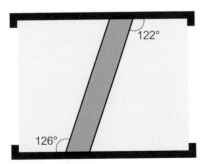

They know their measurements could be up to 5° off.
Could the walls be parallel?

4 P-S / R Look at the diagram.

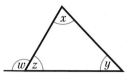

   a Write a formula connecting w and z, beginning $w = ...$
   b Write a formula connecting x, y and z, beginning $z = ...$
   c Using your answers to parts **a** and **b**, prove that the exterior angle in a triangle is equal to the sum of the two opposite interior angles.
   Set out your proof clearly, giving reasons for each step, so that someone else can follow your reasoning.

5 P-S / R

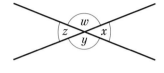

   a Use the diagram to write a formula connecting
      i w and x, beginning $w = ...$
      ii w and z, beginning $z = ...$
   b Use your answers to part **a** to prove that vertically opposite angles are equal.

6 R Which of these diagrams show parallel lines? Give reasons.

   a

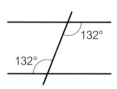

   b

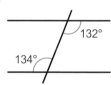

   c

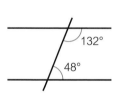

   d

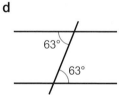

7 P-S / R Use the angles in the diagram to prove that alternate angles are equal.

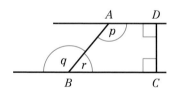

> **Q7 hint** You need to show that alternate angles p and q are equal.
> Start by writing a formula that uses the angles in trapezium $ABCD$.

Reflect

8 Ravi wants to prove that the angles in a triangle add up to 180°.
   He does this by drawing lots of triangles, measuring the angles and showing that they add up to 180°.
   Why has Ravi not proved that the angles in a triangle add up to 180°?

7.3 Angles in parallel lines

- Identify corresponding angles
- Solve problems using properties of angles in parallel and intersecting lines

1 R Work out the angles marked with letters.
Give reasons for your answers.

a
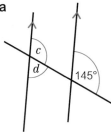

b
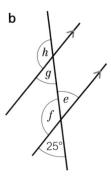

c
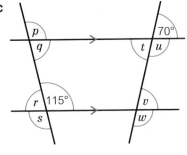

2 R Work out the angles marked with letters.
Give a reason for each answer.

a
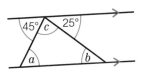

b
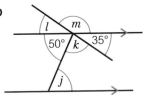

c

d
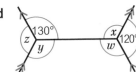

3 R

a Explain why angle a = angle e.

b Which angle is equal to angle b? Explain.

c Which angle is equal to angle f? Explain.

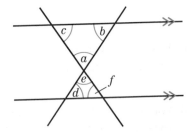

4 R

a Find the angles in triangle CDE. Give reasons.

b Sketch the triangles the same way up.
Label the vertices and angles.

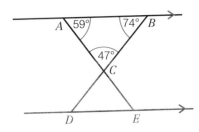

5 R

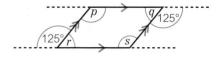

a Write down the sizes of the angles marked with letters. Give reasons.

b What angle facts about parallelograms have you shown?

6 P-S / R The diagram shows two lines intersecting a pair of parallel lines. Work out the sizes of angles a to g. Give reasons for each.

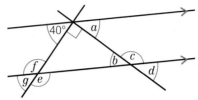

7 R Humphrey and Fatma both work out the size of angle DBC in the diagram.

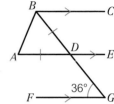

Humphrey:

$BDA = DGF = 36°$ (corresponding angles).
$DAB + ABD + 36° = 180°$ (angles in a triangle).
$DAB = ABD = 144 ÷ 2 = 72°$ (angles in an isosceles triangle).
If I extend line CB to point H, angle $ABH = 72°$ (alternate to BAD).
$DBC = 180 − (72 + 72) = 36°$ (angles on a straight line).

Fatma:

$DGF = DBC = 36°$ (alternate angles).

What did Fatma recognise, that Humphrey did not spot, that allowed her to work this out much more quickly?

Investigation

8 a Work out the sizes of the angles marked with letters.

i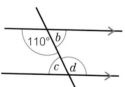

ii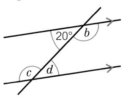

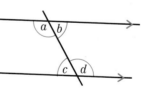

b i Using your answers to part **a**, what can you say about the angles in this diagram?

ii Copy and complete: $a + c = \boxed{}°$ and $b + d = \boxed{}°$.

c What can you say about the sum of the angles marked x and y in this trapezium?

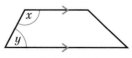

d Will the same be true for any quadrilateral that has parallel sides? Explain your answer. Check your answer by drawing diagrams.

Reflect

9 What advice would you give to someone who is working on an angles question and cannot see how to work out the missing angle?

7.4 Exterior and interior angles

- Calculate the sum of the interior and exterior angles of a polygon
- Work out the sizes of interior and exterior angles of a polygon

1 Work out the unknown angle in each diagram.

a

b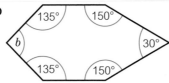

2 **P-S** The sum of the interior angles of a polygon is 2340°.
Work out how many sides it has.

3 Work out the interior angle of a regular:

a hexagon

b nonagon.

4 **P-S** The exterior angle of a
regular polygon is 15°.

a Work out the interior angle.

b How many sides does the polygon have?

Q4b hint ☐ × 15° = ☐°

5 **R** Callie says, 'it is not possible to draw a polygon that has interior angles that sum to
1500°'. Is she correct? Explain your reasoning.

6 The diagram shows two regular octagons.

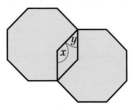

a Work out the size of angle x.

b Work out the size of angle y.

7 A regular polygon has 30 sides. Work out the size of its:

a exterior angle

b interior angle.

c Is it easier to work out the exterior or interior angle of a regular polygon first?

8 P-S / R Sam starts at point O at 11 am.
He waits a minute, then takes a step forward and turns $x°$ clockwise.
He repeats this until, at 12 noon, he arrives back at point O.
Work out the size of angle $x°$.

9 P-S / R The diagram shows parts of some floor tiling using
regular polygons. Work out the angles marked with letters.
Give reasons.

a

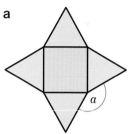

b

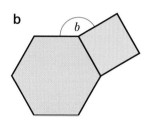

c

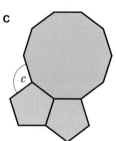

d

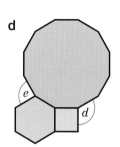

10 P-S The diagram shows a regular hexagon
overlapping with a regular pentagon.
Work out the size of angle y.

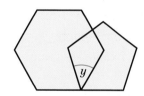

11 R What is the only regular shape with an exterior angle that is greater than the
interior angle?

12 R Is it possible for a regular polygon to have an interior angle that is double the size of the
exterior angle? Give reasons.

13 P-S / R A regular polygon has an interior angle that is 7 times the size of the exterior
angle. How many sides does it have?

14 P-S / R The interior angle of a regular polygon P is equal to $a + b$, where a is the exterior
angle of a regular hexagon and b is the interior angle of a square.
How many sides does polygon P have?

15 P-S / R The diagram shows a regular 12-sided shape
with a triangle inside it.
  a What type of triangle is it?
  b Calculate the size of angle x.

Reflect

16 Why do all polygons have an exterior angle sum of 360°?

7.5 Solving geometric problems

- Solve geometric problems, showing reasoning
- Solve problems involving angles by setting up equations

1   **P-S / R**   The diagram shows the face of a gem stone.
The face has two lines of symmetry. Work out the angle marked x.
Give reasons for your working.

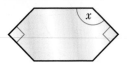

2   The diagram shows triangle ABC.
   a Work out the value of x.
   b Show how to check your value of x is correct.
   c Work out the size of angle y.

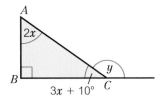

> **Q2b hint** Work out the size of $\angle BAC$ and $\angle ACB$.

3   **P-S**   The diagram shows quadrilateral $ABCD$.
Work out the size of $\angle CDE$.

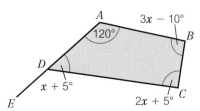

> **Q3 hint** Write an equation in terms of x. Solve your equation to find the value of x.

4   **P-S / R**   In the diagram,
$\angle BAC = \frac{1}{4} \angle BAD$.
Work out the size of $\angle ACD$.
Explain your reasoning.

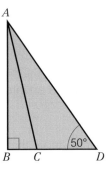

5   **P-S**   The diagram shows four congruent kites that fit exactly around a point.
Angle x is double the size of angle y.
Work out the sizes of angles x and y.
Explain your reasoning.

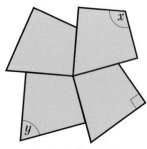

6   **P-S / R**   The diagram shows an irregular pentagon.
Angles x and y are in the ratio 3 : 2.
Work out the sizes of angles x and y.
Explain your reasoning.

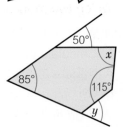

7 The centre of this regular pentagon has been joined to its vertices.

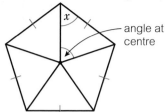

angle at centre

a The lines from the centre are all equal. Explain why.

b i How many angles at the centre are there?

ii Work out the size of each angle at the centre.

iii Work out the angle marked x.

iv How can you use x to work out the interior angle?

c Repeat part **b** for a regular hexagon.

d Write a rule to work out the interior angle from the angle at the centre.

8 R Look at the diagram.
CD is parallel to AB.
Calculate the size of angle ADC.

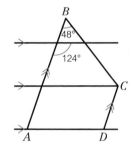

9 P-S / R $ABCD$ is an isosceles trapezium.

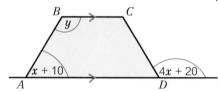

Work out the size of angle y.

10 P-S The diagram shows the interior and exterior angles of a regular polygon.

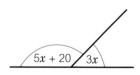

Which two regular polygons could it be?

11 a Is there more than one way to approach Q8?

b Which route to the answer did you prefer?
Did you find it easier to find other routes once you had found the first route?

7 Extend

1   P-S / R   The diagram shows a polygon in the shape of a star.

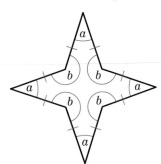

Q1 hint
Work out
the sum of
the interior
angles.

Angle a is 40°. Work out angle b.

2   R   Shapes **tessellate** if they can fit together without any gaps.
   a By talking about their interior angles, explain whether it is possible to make a tessellating pattern using just regular hexagons.
   b Why is it not possible to make a tessellating pattern out of just regular pentagons?
   c Which other regular polygons will tessellate?

3   P-S / R   The diagram shows a regular hexagon.

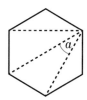

Work out the size of angle a.

4   P-S / R   Place these digits into the sentence below to make it true.

   0   0   0   1   1   2   3   8

   Use each digit exactly once.
   'A polygon with ____ sides has an interior angle sum of _____° and an exterior angle of ____°.'

5   P-S / R   The mean interior angle size of three different regular polygons is 106°.
   a What is the mean exterior angle size?
   b What could the three polygons be?

6 **R** Explain why the sum of the exterior angles drawn on this diagram will be more than 360°.

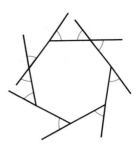

7 **R** The two triangles in the diagram are congruent equilateral triangles.

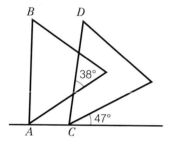

Are the lines AB and CD parallel? Give reasons.

8 **P-S / R** The diagram shows a net of a 3D solid.

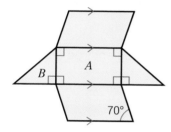

The net is folded to make the solid.
The solid is placed on a table with face A as the base.
Work out the angle between the table and face B.

Investigation

9 In a regular hexagon the interior angle is double the exterior angle.
In a regular octagon the interior angle is triple the exterior angle.
In a regular 16-sided shape the interior angle is 7 times the exterior angle.

  a Find the regular polygons with interior angles that are 4, 5, 6, 8, 9 and 10 times the size of the exterior angle.

  b Is there a pattern? Can you predict the number of sides before you do the calculation?

Reflect

10 What strategies do you apply when you are first looking at a new angle problem?

8 Calculating with fractions

Master   Extend p105

8.1 Ordering fractions

- Order fractions

1   Write these fractions in ascending order.

$\frac{5}{8}$ $\frac{1}{2}$ $\frac{2}{5}$ $\frac{4}{7}$

2   **R**   Athena says '$\frac{3}{14}$ is smaller than $\frac{1}{4}$ because it is smaller than $\frac{3}{12}$.'
    Is Athena correct? Explain your reasons.

3   **R**   Harry says 'the answer to $2 \div 8$ is $\frac{2}{8}$, but he checked his calculator and it gives the answer as $\frac{1}{4}$.'
    a Write the answers to these calculations as fractions.

    i $3 \div 6$ **ii** $2 \div 7$
    iii $6 \div 3$ **iv** $6 \div 4$

    b Write the fractions from part **a** in ascending order.

4   **P-S / R**   Place the digits 3, 4, 2, 8 into the boxes to make the statement true and then write your final fractions in ascending order.

$\frac{\square}{4} > \frac{\square}{\square} < \frac{1}{\square}$

5   Which fraction is closer to 1?

    a $\frac{3}{4}$ or $\frac{4}{3}$ **b** $\frac{5}{6}$ or $\frac{6}{5}$

    c $\frac{7}{8}$ or $\frac{8}{7}$ **d** $\frac{3}{4}$ or $\frac{4}{5}$

6   Clara says,
    'You can compare fractions by finding a common denominator or by finding a common numerator.'

    a Use both methods to rewrite each set of fractions in ascending order.

    i $\frac{4}{7}$ $\frac{3}{8}$ $\frac{2}{15}$ $\frac{12}{27}$
    ii $\frac{8}{12}$ $\frac{23}{24}$ $\frac{17}{36}$ $\frac{11}{18}$

    b R   Which method was easier for each list of fractions?

7   **P-S**   Copy and complete to make this statement true.

$\frac{1}{2} > \frac{2}{\square} > \frac{3}{\square} > \frac{4}{\square} > \frac{5}{\square}$

8 Pedro says 'The answer to $6 \div 7$ is larger than the answer to $11 \div 14$'.
Use fractions to show that Pedro is correct.

9 Which of these fractions are greater than $-\frac{3}{4}$?

$-\frac{3}{8}$ $\qquad$ $-\frac{1}{4}$ $\qquad$ $-\frac{11}{12}$ $\qquad$ $-\frac{1}{3}$

> **Q9 hint** Which fractions lie between $-\frac{3}{4}$ and 0 on a number line?

10 Write these fractions in ascending order.

$-\frac{3}{7}$ $\qquad$ $-\frac{3}{4}$ $\qquad$ $-\frac{5}{8}$ $\qquad$ $-\frac{1}{2}$

11 **P-S / R** Place the digits 3, 4, 2 and 8 into the boxes to make the statement true and then write your final fractions in ascending order.

$-\dfrac{\square}{4} > -\dfrac{\square}{\square} < -\dfrac{1}{\square}$

12 **P-S / R** Find some values for a, b and c so that

$$\frac{a}{c} > \frac{a}{b} > \frac{c}{a+b}$$

13 **P-S / R** Find some values for a, b and c so that

$$\frac{a}{c} > \frac{a}{b} < \frac{c}{a+b}$$

> **Q13 hint** Some of the values can be negative.

14 **R** The numerator of a fraction is increased by 1 and so is the denominator.
Is the new fraction always greater than the original?

15 **R** The numerator of a positive fraction is doubled.
The denominator of the fraction is tripled.
Is the new fraction greater than or less than the original fraction?

16 **R** The numerator of a positive fraction is doubled.
The denominator of the fraction is increased by 10.
When is the new fraction greater than the original fraction?

Reflect

17 When ordering fractions, you can:
- find a common denominator
- find a common numerator
- compare the fractions with an 'easy' fraction like $\frac{1}{4}$, $\frac{1}{2}$ or $\frac{3}{4}$.

When is it best to use each of these methods?

8.2 Adding and subtracting fractions

- Add and subtract fractions with any size denominator

1 **P-S** The diagram shows four fractions linked by lines.

a Work out the total of any two linked fractions.

b Which two fractions give the greatest total?
Write it as a mixed number in its simplest form.

c Work out the difference between any two linked fractions.

d Which two fractions give you the greatest difference?
Write it in its simplest form.

e **R** How did you work out your answers to parts **b** and **d**?

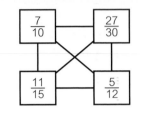

2 Work out these calculations.
Give each answer in its simplest form, and as a mixed number where necessary.

a $\frac{4}{5} + \frac{1}{4} + \frac{1}{2}$ b $\frac{5}{8} + \frac{7}{12} - \frac{11}{24}$ c $\frac{24}{25} - \frac{2}{5} - \frac{13}{50}$

3 How much more than $-\frac{11}{24}$ is $\frac{13}{30}$?

4 This pie chart shows the proportions of workers earning different wages at a company.

a What fraction of workers earn £25 000 or less?

b What fraction of workers earn more than £30 000?

c What is the modal wage group?

d Write down one problem with the way the information is grouped.

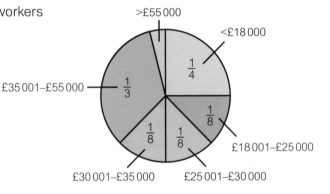

5 **P-S** The table shows the fractions of class 7T that support three different rugby teams.

Rugby team	Scarlets	Blues	Dragons
Fraction of class	$\frac{2}{15}$	$\frac{3}{10}$	$\frac{1}{6}$

a What fraction of the class do not support the Scarlets, Blues or Dragons?

b **R** How many students do you think are in class 7T? Explain your answer.

6 Some red, green and blue counters are mixed together.
$\frac{1}{5}$ of the counters are red, $\frac{2}{7}$ are green.
What is the ratio of red to blue?

7 **P-S** Copy and complete these fraction pyramids.
Each brick is the sum of the two bricks below it.

a

b

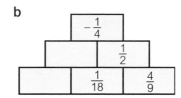

8 The Ancient Egyptians wrote nearly all of their fractions as unit fractions.
They used this eye shape ◯ to show '1 over' a number.

a Use this key to translate these fractions.

Q8 hint A **unit fraction** is a fraction that has a numerator of 1.

Key

$	$ = 1	= 1000	= 100 000
$\cap$ = 10	= 10 000	= 1 000 000
⊙ = 100		

The first one has been done for you.

i ◯/∩ $= \frac{1}{10}$ **ii** **iii** **iv**

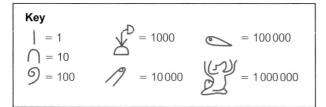

They wrote fractions only as unit fractions (except in special cases).

So, for example, they wrote $\frac{3}{8}$ as ‖‖‖ ‖‖‖‖‖ because it is $\frac{2}{8} + \frac{1}{8} = \frac{1}{4} + \frac{1}{8}$.

The two fractions were always written separately.

b Use Egyptian fractions to write these.

i $\frac{1}{3}$ **ii** $\frac{1}{8}$ **iii** $\frac{5}{6}$ **iv** $\frac{3}{4}$

Investigation

9 Zoe is trying to find out whether all unit fractions can be
written as the sum of two different unit fractions. For example $\frac{1}{2} = \frac{1}{3} + \frac{1}{6}$
She finds that $\frac{1}{9} = \frac{1}{10} + \frac{1}{90}$

a Can you find a rule for writing any unit fraction as the sum of two different unit fractions? Test your rule on different fractions.

b How many different ways can you write $\frac{1}{8}$ as the sum of two different unit fractions?

Reflect

10 In Q7, how did you know if the missing fractions were positive or negative?
What was the same and what was different about the calculation you did to work out missing positive and missing negative fractions?

8.3 Multiplying fractions

- Multiply integers and fractions by a fraction
- Use appropriate methods for multiplying fractions

1 $\frac{1}{6}$ of the members of a school committee are students. $\frac{3}{4}$ of these students are girls. What fraction of the committee are girls?

2 Calculate

a $\frac{8}{3} \times -\frac{3}{8}$

b $\frac{5}{9} \times \frac{18}{10}$

c $\frac{-13}{54} \times \frac{108}{-26}$

d $\frac{2x}{y} \times \frac{y}{2x}$

e Create two more questions that use the same idea.

3 Calculate

a $\left(-\frac{2}{7}\right)^2$

b $\left(-\frac{2}{7}\right)^3$

c $\frac{7}{16} \times \left(-\frac{2}{7}\right)^2$

d $\frac{7}{16} \times \left(-\frac{2}{7}\right)^3$

> **Q3a hint** $\left(-\frac{2}{7}\right)^2 = -\frac{2}{7} \times -\frac{2}{7}$

4 A company pays a fee of £3000 to use a song in an advertisement.
There are three people in the band.
The writer gets $\frac{4}{12}$ of the fee, the singer gets $\frac{1}{12}$ and the guitarist gets $\frac{1}{12}$.
a What fraction of the fee does the whole band get?
b How much money does each member of the band receive?

5 Work out

a $\left(\frac{1}{2} + \frac{1}{3}\right) \times \left(\frac{1}{3} + \frac{1}{4}\right)$

b $\left(\frac{1}{2} + \frac{1}{3}\right) \times \left(\frac{1}{3} - \frac{1}{4}\right) \times \left(\frac{1}{4} + \frac{1}{5}\right)$

Give your answers as fractions in their simplest forms.

6 **P-S** Work out the missing values.

a

Area $= \frac{1}{9}$ cm²

☐ cm

b

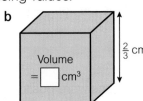

$\frac{2}{3}$ cm

Volume $= $ ☐ cm³

c

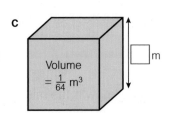

☐ m

Volume $= \frac{1}{64}$ m³

7 R

a Work out

   i $\frac{1}{2}$ of £30 and then $\frac{1}{3}$ of the answer   **ii** $\frac{1}{3}$ of £30 and then $\frac{1}{2}$ of the answer.

   iii What do you notice about your answers to parts **i** and **ii**?
      What is the overall fraction of £30 that you have found?
      How can you combine $\frac{1}{2}$ and $\frac{1}{3}$ to give you this overall fraction?

b Work out

   i $\frac{3}{4}$ of £80 and then $\frac{2}{5}$ of the answer   **ii** $\frac{2}{5}$ of £80 and then $\frac{3}{4}$ of the answer.

   iii What is the overall fraction of £80 that you have found?
      How can you combine $\frac{2}{5}$ and $\frac{3}{4}$ to give you this overall fraction?

c Will your method for parts **a iii** and **b iii** work for any fraction of an amount followed by a fraction of an amount?

8 P-S   Martha spends $\frac{1}{4}$ of her pocket money on food.
She spends $\frac{3}{5}$ of what is left on clothes. She saves the rest.
What fraction of her money does she save?

9 P-S / R $\frac{3}{7}$ of the people at a football match support the away team.
$\frac{3}{4}$ of the home team supporters are season-ticket holders.
What fraction of the people at the match were home team supporters who did not have a season ticket?

10 P-S   The mean of five fractions is $-\frac{1}{4}$.
A fifth fraction is added and the mean of the new set of fractions is 0.
What is the fifth fraction?

Investigation

11 These are the tickets on a jacket that is reduced in price in a sale.

Hint Choose any price for the jacket. Work out the sale price then the price after the further reduction.

a What is the total fraction off the normal price?

b What is the final price as a fraction of the normal price?

c Investigate other calculations involving normal and sale prices, such as $\frac{1}{2}$ off normal price then $\frac{3}{4}$ off sale price. How can you work out the total fraction off for any pair of fractions?

Reflect

12 Hassan says, 'When you multiply a positive integer by a fraction less than 1, your answer will always be less than the number you started with'.

a Is Hassan correct? Explain why.

b Is Hassan's statement correct if you are multiplying a negative integer by a fraction less than 1?

8.4 Dividing fractions

- Find the reciprocal of a number
- Divide integers and fractions by a fraction
- Use strategies for dividing fractions

1 **P-S** Sort these cards into five groups of correct calculations.
There must be one triangular, one rectangular and one circular card in each group.

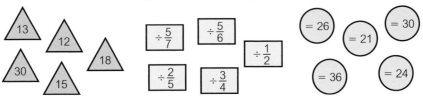

2 **R**

  a What is the product of a number and its reciprocal?

  b Does 0 have a reciprocal? Explain.

3 **P-S** Work out

$$\frac{1}{\left(\frac{1}{2}\right)} + \frac{2}{\left(\frac{1}{3}\right)} + \frac{3}{\left(\frac{1}{4}\right)}$$

> **Q3 hint** $\dfrac{1}{\left(\frac{1}{2}\right)} = 1 \div \frac{1}{2}$

4 **R** Arthur says that when you divide fractions, you can write them with a common denominator and then divide the numerators.
For example, you can write $\frac{3}{4} \div \frac{1}{2}$ as $\frac{3}{4} \div \frac{2}{4}$ and then work out $3 \div 2 = \frac{3}{2}$.

  a Does Arthur's method work? Explain.

  b Do you prefer Arthur's method, or the normal method of dividing fractions? Why?

5 $\frac{3}{4}$ of a number is 18.
What was the original number?

6 Write three different divisions that each give an answer of $\frac{2}{3}$.
Each division should use two fractions.

7 **P-S** Use the digits 1, 2, 3, 4, 6 and 9 to complete this calculation.

$$\frac{\Box}{\left(\frac{\Box}{\Box}\right)} \div \frac{\Box}{\Box} = \Box$$

8 **P-S** The area of a triangle is $\frac{3}{5}$ cm².
The base is 3 cm long.
What is the height?

9 **P-S / R** The area of the rectangle is 3 times the area of the triangle.

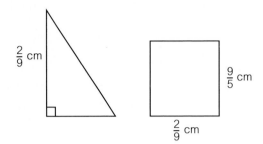

$\frac{2}{9}$ cm

$\frac{9}{5}$ cm

$\frac{2}{9}$ cm

What is the base length of the triangle?

10 Calculate the mean of these fractions.

$\frac{1}{2}$ $\frac{3}{4}$ $-\frac{2}{3}$ $-\frac{3}{4}$

11 **P-S** Place the digits 3, 4, 5 in the boxes so that the mean of the three fractions is greater than $\frac{2}{3}$.

$\frac{\square}{3}$ $\frac{\square}{6}$ $\frac{1}{\square}$

12 Work out the value of x.

a $\frac{2}{3}x = \frac{1}{4}$ **b** $\frac{3}{4}x = \frac{1}{4}$ **c** $\frac{5}{8}x = \frac{5}{6}$

> **Q12a hint**
>
>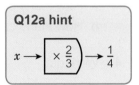
>
> $x \rightarrow \boxed{\times \frac{2}{3}} \rightarrow \frac{1}{4}$

13 **P-S** Work out

$$\frac{\left(\frac{3}{4}\right)}{\left(\frac{2}{3} \div \frac{5}{7}\right)}$$

14 **P-S / R** By choosing values for a, b, c and d, decide whether this statement is always true, sometimes true, or never true.

$$\frac{a}{b} \div \frac{c}{d} > \frac{a \div c}{b \div d}$$

Reflect

15 Multiplication and division are inverse operations.
How did you use your knowledge of multiplying fractions to answer questions in this lesson on dividing fractions? Give examples.

8.5 Calculating with mixed numbers

- Write a mixed number as an improper fraction
- Use the four operations with mixed numbers

1 Work out

$$\left(1 + \frac{1}{2}\right) \times \left(1 + \frac{1}{3}\right) \times \left(-1 + \frac{1}{4}\right)$$

2 **P-S** Work out the area of region B of this rectangle.

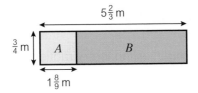

3 **P-S** Jayne cuts pieces of ribbon $\frac{5}{8}$ m in length from a roll of ribbon $13\frac{4}{5}$ m long.

   a How many pieces of ribbon can Jayne cut from this roll?

   b How many centimetres of ribbon does Jayne have left?

4 Work out

   a $1\frac{1}{2} + 2\frac{2}{3} + 3\frac{5}{6}$ b $4\frac{4}{5} + 1\frac{7}{10} + 2\frac{7}{20}$ c $7\frac{3}{4} + 5\frac{2}{9} + 4\frac{11}{12}$

5 Work out the perimeter of each shape.

   a

   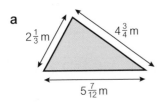

   b

   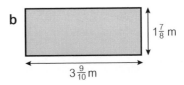

6 These are the ages of the five members of a family.

   $42\frac{1}{2}$ $38\frac{2}{3}$ $14\frac{5}{6}$ $12\frac{5}{12}$ $8\frac{3}{4}$

   Work out the mean age.

7 **P-S** Work out

$$\frac{4\frac{3}{13} + 8\frac{6}{7}}{5\frac{1}{14} - 2\frac{2}{14}} + 1$$

   Give your answer as a mixed number.

8 **P-S** This rectangle has a perimeter of $10\frac{5}{6}$ cm.
Work out the area of the rectangle.
Give your answer as a fraction in its simplest form.

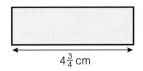

$4\frac{3}{4}$ cm

9 **P-S** Larry thinks of a mixed number.
He multiplies it by 2.
Then he subtracts $5\frac{1}{2}$.
Then he divides by 3.
His answer is $-\frac{4}{5}$.
What is Larry's original number?

10 **P-S** When $3\frac{5}{6}$ is added to a number, the answer is positive.

When the number is cubed, the answer is negative.
When the number is multiplied by $-\frac{2}{3}$, the answer is between 0 and 1.
What could the number be?

11 **P-S / R** Copy and complete these calculations.

a $\sqrt{14\frac{3}{5} + \Box} = 5$ **b** $\sqrt{14\frac{3}{5} + \Box} = 6$

c $\sqrt{14\frac{3}{5} - \Box} = 3$ **d** $\sqrt{14\frac{3}{5} \times \Box} = 5$

Investigation

12 Fencing is sold in lengths of $\frac{3}{4}$ of a metre.
You have 18 lengths that you can use to make a rectangle.
You do not have to use all of the lengths of fencing.

a What is the area of the largest rectangle you can make?

b Investigate what happens to the maximum area each time you add two extra lengths of fencing.

c Predict how your answer to part **b** would change if the fence were sold in different fractions of a metre, and then test your predictions.

Reflect

13 In Q9, how did you use:
- inverse operations
- improper fractions
- your knowledge of negative numbers?

8 Extend

1 **P-S / R** Sierpinski's triangle is a fractal, which means that when you zoom in, each small part looks the same.

a This is the first step for making Sierpinski's triangle.

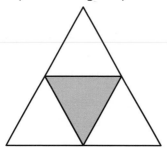

What fraction of this triangle is shaded?

b This is the second step in making Sierpinski's triangle

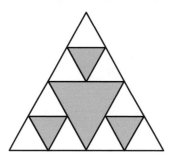

> **Q1b hint** Imagine splitting the big shaded triangle into four smaller triangles. How many smaller triangles are there altogether?

Add the fraction taken up by the big shaded triangle to the fraction taken up by the three smaller triangles to work out the total fraction that is shaded.

c Draw the third step in making Sierpinski's triangle.
Write down the three fractions you need to add together to work out the total fraction that is shaded.

d Describe the sequence made by the numerators and the sequence made by the denominators.

e Do you think the whole triangle will ever be shaded?

Investigation

2 The diagram shows an area puzzle.

a Calculate the area of region A.

b Create your own area puzzle that has a final solution that is the same as for the puzzle above. Use at least four rectangles and give as little information as possible.

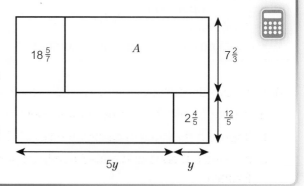

3 **P-S** One eighth of a rectangular swimming pool is filled with water.
The sun heated the pool and two thirds of the water in the pool evaporated.
There was $78\frac{1}{8}$ m³ of water left in the pool.
How much water would be in the pool if it was full?

4 **P-S** Write this expression as a single fraction:

$$\left(\frac{a}{b} \div \frac{c}{d}\right) \div \frac{e}{f}$$

5 **P-S / R** Alphonse wants to know how many marks he needs to get in his final exam to pass the course.
In his first exam, he got $\frac{82}{90}$.
In his second exam, he got $\frac{15}{28}$.
In his third exam, he got $\frac{32}{43}$.
The final exam is out of 65.
In order to pass the course, he must get at least $\frac{3}{4}$ of the marks overall, across the four exams.
How many marks does he need to get in his final exam to pass the course?

6 A sequence starts $\frac{4}{5}$, $\frac{3}{4}$, ...
It is formed by multiplying each term by a number to get the next term.
a What is the number that terms are multiplied by?
b What is the third term?
c **R** Will the sequence ever reach 0? Explain.

7 **P-S** A wall is 8 m long. $\frac{1}{16}$ of it is painted.
When 2.5 m² more is painted, $\frac{1}{6}$ of the wall will be painted.
How high is the wall?

8 **P-S / R** Are there integers a, b, c and d for which this statement is true?
$$\frac{a}{b} + \frac{c}{d} = \frac{a+c}{b+d}$$

Investigation

9 **a** Calculate $1 - \frac{1}{2} + \frac{1}{3} - \frac{1}{4}$.
b Add $\frac{1}{5}$ to your answer.
c Subtract $\frac{1}{6}$.
d Continue the pattern. What do you notice?

Reflect

10 Is it more difficult, the same, or easier to work with:
a proper fractions or improper fractions? Explain.
b improper fractions or mixed numbers? Explain.
c positive fractions and mixed numbers or negative fractions and mixed numbers? Explain.

9 Straight-line graphs

Master   Extend p113

9.1 Direct proportion on graphs

- Recognise when values are in direct proportion with or without a graph
- Plot graphs and read values to solve problems

1 An electrician charges a call-out fee and then an hourly rate.
Some of her charges are shown in the table.

Time (hours)	2.5	3.5	5
Cost (£)	77.50	92.50	115

   a Draw a graph to show this information.

   b What is the electrician's call-out fee?

   c What is her hourly rate?

   d R Are time and cost in direct proportion? Explain.

2 R The graph shows two mobile phone
payment plans.

   a How much does it cost for 1 GB data on:

     i Plan A   **ii** Plan B?

   b For how much data do both plans cost the
same?

Data costs

   c Are data use and cost in direct proportion
for both Plan A and Plan B? Explain.

   d Copy the graph. Draw a new Plan C, where data use and cost are in direct proportion.

   e Write a short paragraph advising a customer which plan to choose, based on their data
usage and best value for money.

3 R The table shows the
number of ice creams

Number of ice creams sold	1	2	3	4	5	6
Income (£)	0.50	1	1.50	2	2.50	3

sold by an ice cream seller, and her income.

   a Is the number of ice creams sold in direct proportion to income?

   b Draw a graph showing this data.

   c The table shows the cost
to the ice cream seller of
making ice creams.

Number of ice creams	1	2	3	4	5	6
Cost to make (£)	0.20	0.40	0.60	0.80	1	1.20

     i Draw a graph showing this information on the same set of axes as in part **b**.

     ii Calculate the profit made from each ice cream.
Is profit made in direct proportion to the number of ice creams sold?

     iii Draw a graph showing the profit against number of ice creams sold.

   d It costs the ice cream seller £300 a week to rent her ice cream machine.

     i Is the cost of making ice creams still in direct proportion to the number sold?

     ii **P-S** The ice cream machine can make 25 ice creams in one hour.
How many hours does the machine need to be operating, in a week, to make a profit
(assuming the ice cream seller sells all the ice creams the machine makes)?

4 **P-S / R** A gardening company charges £160 for the first hour of work on a garden.
They charge £50 per hour after the first hour.
If they work for more than 5 hours, they charge all hours, including the first hour, at £65.
   a Draw a graph showing the costs from 0 to 10 hours of work.
   b When is the amount of work in direct proportion to the amount the company is charging?

5 **R** Ben runs at a constant speed of 11 km/h.
The graph shows Ben's run.
   a Explain why this graph does not show direct proportion.
   b Ginny runs at a constant speed of 10 km/h.
   Copy and complete the table for Ginny's run.

Ben's run

Time (hours)	0	0.5	1	1.5	2
Distance travelled (km)	0				

   c Draw a graph showing Ginny's run.
   d Use the graphs to complete the table.

Time (hours)	0	0.5	1	1.5	2
Distance between Ginny and Ben (km)					

   e Is the distance between Ginny and Ben in direct proportion
   to the amount of time?
   Explain why.

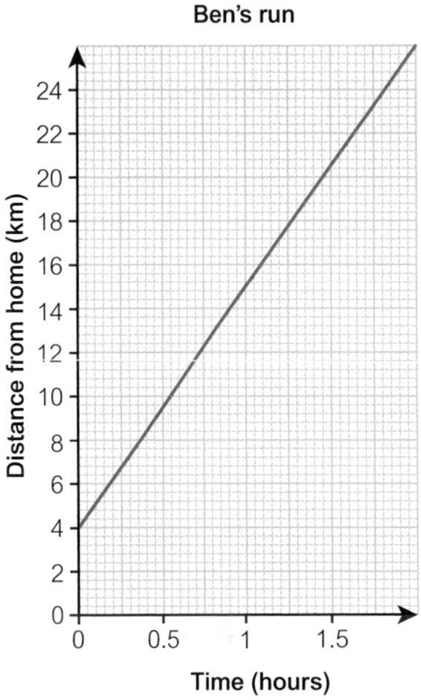

6 **R** A and B are in direct proportion. B and C are in direct proportion.
Explain whether A and C would be in direct proportion.

Investigation

7 Lucy says that the area of a rectangle is in direct proportion to the perimeter.
Start with a rectangle that measures 3 cm by 4 cm and calculate its perimeter and area.
Increase the sides by 1 cm each and recalculate.
Repeat this five times and look for direct proportion.
Consider other ways you can systematically investigate this.
Is Lucy's theory always, sometimes, or never true?

8 **P-S / R** Are these measures directly proportional? Explain.
   a Edge length of a cube and its volume
   b Edge length of a regular polygon and its perimeter
   c Base length of a parallelogram and its area,
       where base length = perpendicular height

Reflect

9 Describe a situation where two quantities are sometimes, but not always, in direct
proportion.

9.2 Gradients

- Plot a straight-line graph and work out its gradient

1 **a** For each table of values, state whether the variables are in direct proportion.

i

x	0	1	2	3	4
y	0	2	4	6	8

ii

x	0	1	2	3	4
y	1	3	5	7	9

iii

x	0	1	2	3	4
y	2	−2	−6	−10	−14

iv

x	1	2	3	4	5
y	3	6	9	12	15

   b Plot the graphs from parts **i** to **iv** on separate sets of axes.

2 **R** For each table in Q1, divide the y-values by the corresponding x-values.

   a What do you notice about the relationship between variables and those that give a constant answer?

   b Compare your answers to part **a** to the gradient of each graph.
   What do you notice?

3 **a** **i** Plot a graph using the x- and y-values in the table.

   ii Work out the gradient of your graph from part **i**.

x	−2	−1	0	1	2
y	−8	−5	−2	1	4

   b **i** Swap the x- and y-values and draw a new graph on the same set of axes.

   ii Work out the gradient.

   c **i** Plot a graph on a new set of axes using the x- and y-values in this table.

x	−2	−1	0	1	2
y	−2	0	2	4	6

   ii Work out the gradient.

   d **i** Swap the x- and y-values and draw a new graph on the same set of axes.

   ii Work out the gradient.

   e **i** Plot a graph on a new set of axes using the x- and y-values in this table.

x	−2	−1	0	1	2
y	−6	−2	2	6	10

   ii Work out the gradient.

   f **i** Swap the x- and y-values and draw a new graph on the same set of axes.

   ii Work out the gradient.

   g **R** Each graph, with variables swapped, is a reflection of the original graph.

   i Draw the mirror line for the reflection on each pair of axes.

   ii Work out the gradient of the mirror lines.
   What do you notice?

4 a Use the graph to complete this table.

x	-2	-1	0	1	2
y-values (A)					
y-values (B)					

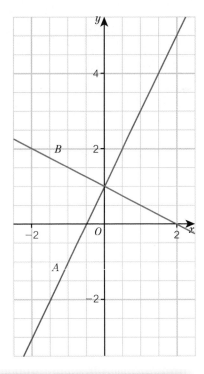

b What is the gradient of each line?

c What is the mathematical relationship between the two lines?

Investigation

x	-2	-1	0	1	2
y	-3	-1	1	3	5

5 a Plot the graph from the table.

b What is the gradient?

c Increase all of the y-values by 1. Does the gradient change?

d Test this idea by increasing and decreasing all of the y-values by a new amount.

e What happens to the gradient when all of the y-values are increased or decreased by the same amount?

f Multiply all of the y-values by 3. Does the gradient change?

g Test this idea by multiplying and dividing all the y-values by a new amount.

h What happens to the gradient when all the y-values are multiplied or divided by the same amount?

i Increase all of the y-values by 10%. Does the gradient change?

j What happens to the gradient when all the y-values are changed by the same percentage?

k Sarah says, 'In parts **h**, **i** and **j** you are doing the same thing to the gradient'. What do you think she means?

Reflect

6 You have seen lines like this on graphs:

  C _____

a Which of these lines could show a direct proportion relationship?

b Which line has the gradient closest to 0?

c What is different about the gradients of A and B?

9.3 Equations of straight lines

- Plot the graphs of linear functions
- Write the equations of straight-line graphs in the form $y = mx + c$

1 A law firm has collected the data on the monthly pay for staff.

Number of new clients (x)	0	5	10	15	20
Pay (£y)	1750	1850	1950	2050	2150

a Draw the graph of this data.

The pay includes a basic payment (£), and then an amount (£) for every new client.

b What is the basic payment?

c Write an equation linking the number of new clients to the monthly pay for staff.

Q1b hint What is the pay when there are no new clients?

2 In which of these equations are x and y in direct proportion?

a $y = 2x - 5$ b $y = -4x$ c $y = 6x$

d $y = \frac{1}{3}x$ e $y = -\frac{1}{2}x + 2$

Q2 hint When two quantities are in direct proportion, where does the graph cross the y-axis?

3 For each of the equations given, draw a table of values and use it to plot the graph.

Use your graphs to copy and complete this table.

How can you find the gradient and y-intercept of a line without plotting the graph?

Equation of line	Gradient	y-intercept
$y = 2x - 5$		
$y = x + 1$		
$y = 3x + 4$		
$y = -x + 2$		
$y = -2x - 7$		
$y = \frac{1}{3}x + 1$		

4 An advertising company uses a graph of this equation to work out the cost of making an advert:

$y = 10 + 0.5x$

x is the number of words and y is the total cost in pounds.

a Where does the line cross the y-axis?

b What is the cost when there are no words in the advert?

c What is the gradient of the line?

d How much does each word cost?

5   P-S
    a Draw a coordinate grid and plot the points (3, 5) and (1, −1).
    b Join them with a straight line. Extend it to the edge of the grid.
    c Write the equation of the line in the form $y = mx + c$.

6   P-S   A rectangle is made using four straight lines.

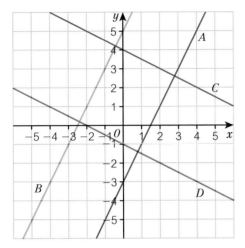

The equation of line A is $y = 2x − 3$.
Write the equations of the other three lines.

7   R   A line has a gradient of −2 and crosses the y-axis at $(0, \frac{1}{2})$.
    a What is the equation of this line?
    b Use the equation to make a table of values and plot the graph.
    c Reflect the line in the y-axis. What is the equation of the new line?
    d Reflect the original line in the x-axis. What is the equation of the new line?
    e Reflect the original line in the line $y = x$. What is the equation of the new line?
    f Using a table of values, plot the line $y = 3 − 2x$.
    g What is the relationship between the original line and $y = 3 − 2x$?
    h Plot the line $2y = 3 + x$.
    i What is the relationship between the original line and $2y = 3 + x$?

8   P-S / R   Decide if each statement about the line $y = \frac{1}{2}x − 7$ is true or false.
    a It has a gradient of 0.5.
    b It is parallel to $2y = x + 12$.
    c It is steeper than $y = \frac{1}{3}x − 7$.
    d It crosses the y-axis at (0, 7).
    e It is a reflection of $y = −\frac{1}{2}x + 7$ in the y-axis.

9   A line has gradient of 4 and meets the y-axis at (0, −3). Write the equation of the line.

Reflect

10 Look back at Q8. Write a sentence explaining how you decided if each statement was
    true or false. Compare your explanations with others in your class.

9 Extend

1 **a** Work out the gradient of this line.

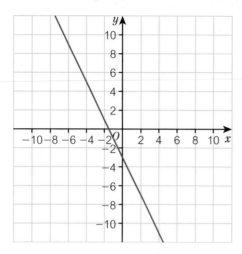

    b Write the equation of the line in the form $y = mx + c$.

2 **R** The table shows the number of hours worked and the pay.

Hours	1	2	3	4	5
Pay	£8.50	£17	£25.50	£34	£42.50

    a Draw a graph to show this information.

    b A person works for 4.5 hours.
        How much will they get paid?

    c One person earns £2 extra for the first hour they work.
        Are the values still in direct proportion?

    d A second person gets a 10% an hour pay rise.
        Are the values still in direct proportion?

    e A third person gets their hourly pay tripled.
        Are the values still in direct proportion?

3 Graph 1 has a gradient of $\frac{1}{2}$ and goes through the point $A\,(1, 2)$.
    a What is the equation of Graph 1?

    b Graph 1 is reflected in the x-axis to make Graph 2.
      i What is the equation of Graph 2?
     ii What are the new coordinates of point A?

    c Graph 2 is reflected in the y-axis to make Graph 3.
      i What is the equation of Graph 3?
     ii What are the new coordinates of point A?

    d R Is there a single transformation that transforms Graph 3 to Graph 1?
        If so, what is it?

4 **R** A YouTuber has recorded how many views they get compared to how many new videos they release in a week.

New videos	0	1	2	3
Views (nearest 1000)	2000	3000	4000	5000

    a Is the number of views in direct proportion to the number of videos?

    b Plot the graph.

    c Find an equation linking the number of views to the number of new videos in a week.

    d Do you think that if the YouTuber released 18 new videos in a week they would get 20 000 views? Explain your reasoning.

    e The number of views is rounded to the nearest 1000.
       Would you expect that the real number of views compared to the number of videos would form a linear graph? Explain your reasoning.

5 **P-S** Two lines are reflections of each other in the y-axis.
Two of the following points are on one of the lines and the other two points are on the other line:
$(-1, 1)$, $(2, 3)$, $(-3, 5)$ and $(-3, -7)$
State the equations of the two lines and their point of intersection.

6 **R** Dany says,
'If you reflect a graph in the y-axis, the two graphs will always cross at their y-intercepts.'
Is Dany correct? Explain your reasoning.

7 **R** A graph is reflected in the x-axis. What point on the graph will stay in the same place?

8 **P-S** Three squares are drawn on a coordinate grid as shown.
The first square has an area of 16 units².
The second square has an area of 36 units².
The third square has an area of 81 units².
A straight line is drawn through vertices A and C.
What is the equation of the straight line?

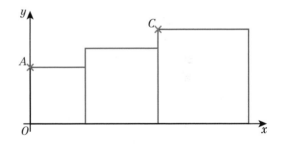

Investigation

9 In Q3 you looked at the impact of reflections in the x- and y-axes on the equations of graphs.
By drawing different graphs, find the equations of five graphs where the reflection in the x-axis is the same as the reflection in the y-axis.

Reflect

10 Why do you think it is important to know if two quantities are in direct proportion, or not? How might you use this outside of the classroom?

10 Percentages, decimals and fractions

Master　　　　Extend p123

10.1 Fractions and decimals

- Change time to decimal hours
- Recognise recurring and terminating decimals
- Order fractions by converting them to decimals or equivalent fractions

1　Convert these times in minutes to fractions of hours.

　　a 150 minutes　　　**b** 45 minutes　　　**c** 75 minutes　　　**d** 18 minutes

 2　Use your calculator to convert these decimal hours to hours and minutes.

　　a 2.5 hours　　　**b** 0.3 hours

　　c 8.2 hours　　　**d** 1.7 hours

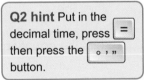
> **Q2 hint** Put in the decimal time, press $=$ then press the ○ ’ ” button.

 3　**a** A researcher says that if fewer than 2 in 5 councillors on a single council are female, that is evidence of discrimination.

　　b R How does your answer to part **a** tell you that 50 minutes written in decimal hours is also a recurring decimal? Write the recurring decimal.

　　c Which multiples of 5 minutes are recurring decimals when written in decimal hours, and which are terminating decimals?

4　**R** The time an event took is a recurring decimal when written as a decimal number of hours.
　　It is greater than 3 hours and less than 4 hours.
　　It is closer to 4 hours than to 3 hours.
　　How many hours and how many minutes could the event have taken?

 5　Write these in ascending order.

　　1.4%　　$\frac{4}{5}$　　0.7%　　1.1%　　$\frac{1}{20}$　　$\frac{3}{85}$　　4.1%　　$\frac{1}{68}$　　$0.\dot{8}$

 6　**P-S** This cake recipe is for 12 people. Work out how much of each ingredient is needed for a cake for 7 people.

flour	160 g
butter	170 g
sugar	180 g
eggs	4
vanilla	50 ml

7 **R** A factory makes scooters.
It has four production lines, A, B, C and D.
The table shows the numbers of perfect scooters and defective scooters produced on each production line on one day.

Production line	Number of perfect scooters	Number of defective scooters	Fraction of scooters that are defective
A	460	40	
B	543	57	
C	370	30	
D	279	21	

  a Copy and complete the table to show the fraction of scooters that are defective on each production line.
    Write each fraction in its simplest form.
  b **i** Which production line is producing the lowest proportion of defective scooters?
    ii Do you think this is the best production line? Explain your answer.
  c The company model their total production figures on production line A.
    Do you think this is a good production line to use?
    Explain your answer.

8 Work out:
  a $0.\dot{6} + 0.1$ **b** $0.\dot{6} - 0.1$ **c** $0.\dot{6} \times 10$ **d** $6.\dot{6} - 0.6$

Investigation

9 Evie uses her calculator to convert $\frac{1}{9}$ and $\frac{2}{9}$ to decimals.
She writes:
$\frac{1}{9} = 0.111...$ $\frac{2}{9} = 0.222...$
  a Continue Evie's pattern up to $\frac{9}{9}$.
  b Write $\frac{13}{9}$ as a decimal.
  c Investigate fractions with 99 as the denominator.
  Use your answers to write these recurring decimals as fractions:
    i 0.373 737...   **ii** 0.656 565....   **iii** 0.060 606...

10 Work out the difference between 0.2 and...
  a $0.2\dot{1}$ **b** $0.\dot{2}\dot{1}$ **c** $0.20\dot{1}$ **d** $0.\dot{2}0\dot{1}$

Reflect

11 Use 1.0909, $1.0\dot{9}$ and $1.0\dot{9}$ to explain the difference between a terminating decimal with repeating digits and a recurring decimal.

10.2 Equivalent proportions

- Use different methods to find equivalent fractions, decimals and percentages
- Use the equivalence of fractions, decimals and percentages to compare two or more proportions

1   R   The label on a cake says it has 4.2 g of sugar in a 50 g serving.
The label on a brownie says it has 10.4 g of sugar in a 125 g serving.
Which has the higher proportion of sugar?

2   P-S   In 2007 a newspaper reported that the unemployment rate in a country was 38 per 1000 people. In 2010, the country had a population of 52.6 million, with 4.1 million people unemployed. Did the unemployment rate increase from 2007 to 2010?

3   A researcher says that if fewer than 2 in 5 councillors on a single council are female, that is evidence of discrimination.
Council A has 128 councillors and 72 are male.
Council B has 5 female councillors for every 8 male councillors.
30% of the councillors on Council C are female.

a Do any of these councils show evidence of discrimination?

b Which council is closest to 50% male and 50% female?

c Which council has the greatest proportion of females?

4   Three friends are talking about how much food and drink they had at a picnic.
Alima says she ate three sandwiches and drank 1 litre of water
Hoda says she ate five sandwiches and drank 1.25 litres of water
Jemma says she ate one sandwich and drank 0.6 litres of water.

a Who had drank the most water for each sandwich they ate?

b The picnic's host said that they expected people to drink about 0.8 litres of water if they ate two sandwiches. Who drank the amount of water closest to the host's expectations?

5   R   A medical test for a disease produces a 'false positive' for 0.1% of patients.
A new test, developed in trials, falsely identified 5 out of the 190 participants as having the disease.
Is the new test better than the old test at not having false positives?

> **Q5 hint** A **false positive** is a test result that falsely indicates a patient has the disease when they don't.

6   P-S / R   An advertising company claims that its adverts will increase your sales by 30%.
In 2017, Gorgeous Scarves sold 45 scarves in June and 55 scarves in July.
In 2018, Gorgeous Scarves ran an advertising campaign from the company in July.
In June 2018, they sold 80 scarves and in July they sold 120 scarves.
By comparing the proportions of scarves sold in June 2017 and 2018 with July 2017 and 2018, decide whether the advertising campaign in July 2018 met the company's claim.

7 P-S / R   Three football teams are comparing their records.
The Bears won 3 games, drew 2 and lost 5.
They scored 12 goals, saved 54 goals and had 18 goals scored against them.
The Tigers won 6 games, drew 1 and lost 7.
They scored 18 goals, saved 12 goals and had 18 goals scored against them.
The Penguins won 12 games, drew 3 and lost 2.
They scored 12 goals, saved 0 goals and had 2 goals scored against them.
a Which team has the best striker (person who scores goals)? Give a reason.
b Which team has the best goalkeeper? Give a reason.
c Which team is doing the best overall? Give reasons.

8 P-S / R   A global study looked at obesity rates in the United States, the UK and Australia.
In the United States, it was found that 36% of the population are obese.
In the UK, it was found that out of the 66.04 million people, 18.5 million people are obese.
In Australia, out of a sample of 500 people, 145 people were obese.
a Which country has the greatest proportion of obese people, according to this study?
b Do you have enough information from the question to know which country has the greatest number of obese people?
c A second study using a sample of 840 people in the UK found that of the 408 women taking part, 122 were obese. Of the men taking part, 129 were obese.
  i Did females or males in the sample have the greater proportion of obesity?
  ii Write a sentence comparing the results of this study with the results for the UK from the first study.

9 R   Taye says he needs b balls of wool to make a 0.5 m long scarf.
He used c balls of wool to make a shorter scarf.
a Which statement is true?

| **A** $b > c$ | **B** $c > b$ | **C** $c = b$ |

b Taye makes a third scarf.
It is 0.7 m long and uses 5 balls of wool.
As it is narrower, it takes less wool for Taye to make the 0.7 m scarf than it did to make the 0.5 m scarf. Which statement is true?

| **A** $b > 5$ | **B** $b < 5$ | **C** Not enough information to say |

Reflect

10 What method do you use when comparing and interpreting more than two proportions?
Is it the same or different from your method for comparing and interpreting exactly two proportions? Explain.

10.3 Writing percentages

- Express one number as a percentage of another when the units are different
- Work out an amount increased or decreased by a percentage
- Use mental strategies to solve percentage problems

 1 To start a woodwork project, 3 mm is shaved from a 3.2 m long piece of wood. What percentage of the piece of wood is shaved off?

2 **R** Amir wants to buy a 3D TV. He sees this advert. He decides to pay the deposit and monthly payments.
  a How much does he pay in total?
  b Which method is cheaper and by how much?

> **3D TV for Sale!**
> Cash Price £800
> or
> Deposit of 30% of Cash Price
> plus 10 monthly payments of £60

3 **R** Leah wants to buy a moped. She sees this advert. She decides to pay the deposit and monthly payments.
  a How much does she pay in total?
  b How much extra does she pay using this method rather than paying by cash?
  c How much extra does she pay as a percentage of the cash price?

> **BRAND NEW MOPED FOR SALE!**
> Cash Price £1200
> OR
> Deposit of 25% of cash price plus
> 10 monthly payments of £102

4 **R** What different strategies can you use to find 25% of an amount?

Investigation

5 Emily earns £20 000 per year, Gary earns £40 000 per year and Simra earns £100 000 per year.
The Government proposes three different tax policies.
- Policy A: Everyone pays 15% on all the money they earn.
- Policy B: Everyone pays 20% on any money earned above £10 000.
- Policy C: Everyone pays 30% on any money earned above £30 000.
  a Which policy results in the lowest tax for each person?
  b Which policy generates the most tax for the government from these three people?

 6 Kim puts £1250 into an investment that pays 4.85% simple interest per year.
She takes the money out after 4 years and 3 months. What is the value of her investment when she takes her money out?
Give your answer to the nearest penny.

> **Q6 hint** In the final year she only gets 3 months' worth of the yearly amount.

7 **P-S** The area of triangle B is 25% more than the area of triangle A. Work out a possible base length and height of triangle B.

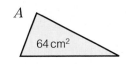

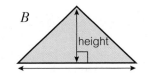

8 Jen wants to invest £800. She sees these rates offered.

a Copy and complete the table to show the simple interest she would earn in each bank.

Year	Savings R Us		Gold Savings		Investor's Delight	
	Interest	Total savings	Interest	Total savings	Interest	Total savings
1						
2						
3						

b **R** What do you notice about the difference in the total amounts as the years progress?

9 Luke buys shares for £15.26 each. They decrease in value by 3.5%.
Work out the new share price.

10 **R** A DIY store advertises a '10% Off Day'.
The next day, prices return to normal.
A competitor says that the prices have gone up 10% in a day.
a Is the competitor right?
b Explain your answer with an example.

11 One way of mentally working out 2.5% of a value is to find 5% and then divide by 2.
Another way is to find 25% and then divide by 10.
a Write two different ways you can mentally work out:
   i 12.5%   **ii** 7.5%   **iii** 17.5%   **iv** 32.5%
b Choose one of your methods from part **a** to increase £200 by each of these percentages.

Reflect

12 In Q11, for each percentage, which of your two different methods do you prefer?
Explain why.

10.4 Percentages of amounts

- Use a multiplier to calculate amounts increased or decreased by a percentage
- Use the unitary method to solve percentage problems

1   **R**   These offers are given by three supermarkets for the same packet of biscuits.

A
12 biscuits for £1.80 plus 25% extra free!

B
12 biscuits for £1.80 Buy 2 packets and get the 3rd half price!

C
12 biscuits for £1.80 Now 25% off!

Which supermarket gives the best offer?
Explain how you made your decision.

2   **R**   Fuel prices have increased by 9% this year.
The Smith family's fuel bill for this year is £1956.

   a How much was the bill likely to have been last year?

   b Why can't you work out exactly how much the bill was last year?

3   **P-S**   The house sparrow population has decreased by 41% since 1977.
The population is now approximately 6.5 million pairs of birds.
Estimate the population of pairs of house sparrows in 1977.

4   **P-S**   A TV programme is edited for broadcasting and 17% of the original programme is cut.
The programme is now $1\frac{1}{2}$ hours long. How long was the original programme?

5   **P-S**   Holiday prices are 14% higher than last year.
A holiday this year costs £940.50. How much would it have cost last year?

6   **P-S**   Chris runs a marathon to raise money for charity.
90% of the money he raises goes to a homeless charity.
The homeless charity receives £270.
How much money did Chris raise?

7   **R**   A shop is having a '5% Off Everything' sale.
Georgia wants to buy six items.
The shop assistant says that, since Georgia is buying six items, the total discount will be 6 × 5% and gives her a 30% total discount.
Explain the mistake the shop assistant has made.

8   Clara says '40% of 30 is the same as 30% of 40.'
    Will this always, sometimes or never work? Explain.

9   R   Between the ages of 3 and 5 years old a tree grows at a rate of approximately
    10% per year.
    At 5 years old it is 2.5 m tall.
    a Work out the height of the tree when it was:
       i 4 years old   ii 3 years old.
       Write each answer correct to the nearest cm.
    b Andy says 'The tree has grown 10% each year for 2 years, which makes 20% in total. This
       means if I divide 2.5 m by 1.2 I will find the height of the tree when it was 3 years old.'
       Is Andy correct? Explain your answer.

10 P-S   Between 2011 and 2012 visitor numbers to a museum increased by 25%.
    Between 2012 and 2013 visitor numbers to the museum decreased by 10%.
    In 2013 there were 71 856 visitors.
    How many visitors were there in 2011?

11 P-S x is 20% more than y.
    y is 30% less than z.
    $z = 4200$.
    Work out the value of x.

12 P-S / R   One side length of a rectangle is increased by 10%.
    The other side length is reduced by 10%.
    By what percentage has the area of the rectangle changed?

13 P-S / R   The area of a rectangle has decreased by 2%.
    The length of one side was increased by 10%.
    By what percentage was the other side reduced?
    Give your answer correct to the nearest integer.

14 P-S / R   Shorifa is writing a book.
    Every day she writes 2% fewer words than she wrote the day before.
    a On the sixth day she wrote 1200 words.
       How many words did she write on the first day?
    b How many words did Shorifa write on the fourth day?
    c Will Shorifa ever stop writing? Explain.

Reflect

15 a Write the steps you would use to find the original amount after a decrease of 5% and
       then an increase of 10%.
    b What would be the same, and what would be different, when finding the original
       amount after an increase of 5% and then a decrease of 10%?

10 Extend

1 P-S Baz paid £18 for a pair of shoes.
He lists them for sale online, but after a week no one has bought them.
Baz reduces the price by 7%.
Someone buys the shoes and Baz makes a 14% profit.
What price did Baz originally list the shoes online for?

2 P-S James, John and Jasmine are having lunch together.
James pays 36% of the bill, John pays 40% of the remainder and Jasmine pays what is left, which is £12.
How much is the whole bill?

3 P-S Brian invests £300 in an account that pays 4.35% simple interest per year.

a How much money will he have after the first year?

b How much money will he have after 5 years?

c Most banks pay compound interest.
Copy and complete the table to show how much money Brian will have after 5 years of compound interest.

> **Key point**
>
> In **compound interest** the interest earned in the first year is added and then earns interest in the next year.

> **Q3c hint** Keep the exact answer in your calculator. Write down the amount to the nearest penny.

Year	Money at start of year	Interest rate	Money at end of year
1	£300	4.35%	£300 × 1.0435 = £313.05
2	£313.05	4.35%	£313.05 × 1.0435 =
3		4.35%	
4		4.35%	
5		4.35%	

d R Compare the final amount after 5 years with simple interest and with compound interest. What do you notice?

4 P-S Esther is getting faster and faster at completing her times-table challenge.
She is getting 20% faster each week.
This week she took 50 seconds to finish the challenge.
How long did she take 3 weeks ago?

5 P-S / R The mean of the ages of the three people in a room is 16.
Another person enters the room and the mean age increases by 25%.
How old is the new person?

6 P-S Rachel is looking at her test scores for maths.
In her second test, she got 30% more than in her first test.
In her third test she got 15% less than in her second test.
In her fourth test, Rachel scored 12% more than in her third test.
Did Rachel do better in her fourth test than in her first test?

7 **P-S / R** In 2008, Jerry planted some flower seeds and 70% of them bloomed.
In 2009, Jerry planted 20% fewer seeds but 90% of them bloomed.
a In which year did Jerry have more blooming plants?
b In 2010, Jerry planted 15% more seeds than in 2009 and one eighth did not bloom.
Did Jerry get more flowers in 2010 than in 2008?

Investigation

8 **a** Show that the solution to $9x = 1.5$ is $x = \frac{1}{6}$.
b Convert x to a decimal, showing how the decimal places recur.
c Multiply your answer by 10. What happens to the decimal places?
d Subtract your original number. What happens to the decimal places?
e Let y represent the decimal $0.\dot{2}$.
Use the method from parts **c** and **d** to work out the value of $9y$ and write y as
a fraction. Use the equation $9x = 1.5$ to help you.
f Use the same method to convert each of these recurring decimals into a fraction.
i 0.444 44...   **ii** 0.555 55...   **iii** 0.777 77...   **iv** 0.888 88...   **v** 0.999 99...

9 **P-S** There are 42% more oranges than apples in a basket.
a What is the ratio of oranges to apples?
b What is the smallest number of oranges there could be?

Investigation

10 The 'half-life' of a drug is how long it takes for the body to remove half of
the amount. The half-life of caffeine is roughly 6 hours.
a What percentage of the caffeine would be left after   **i**   6 hours   **ii**   12 hours?
b A person drank a cup of coffee that contained 94.8 mg of caffeine.
Approximately how long will it be until they have less than 1 mg of caffeine
in their body?
c The table shows some other caffeinated drinks.
For each drink, work out approximately how long it will take for the amount of caffeine
in the body to fall to less than 1 mg after drinking one serving.

Drink	Caffeine in 100 ml	Serving size
Tea	11 mg	238 ml
Diet fizzy drink	12.96 mg	300 ml
Fizzy drink	8 mg	300 ml
Energy drink	30 mg	258 ml

d A person drinks a cup of coffee and then 6 hours later drinks a cup of tea.
Approximately how long will it take until they have less than 1 mg of caffeine
left in their body?

Reflect

11 What do you think are the three most important facts you have learned about
percentages in this unit? Explain why you chose these facts.

Answers

Unit 1 Number

1.1 Calculations

1 Estimate £6.35 to be £6.50 or £7 as we need to round up for money. Georgina does not have enough money. Other answers possible.

2 **a** £6715 **b** £559.58

3 300 × 2.5 = 750 km

4 Calculation A is incorrect.

5 **a** 0.12 **b** 0.12
   c This will always happen provided you keep the sign with the term. The order of addition and subtraction does not matter as addition is commutative.
   d 0.04

6 30 × 12 = 360, 15 × 12 = 180, 15 × 13 = 195, 15 × 14 = 210, 15 × 15 = 225

7 £322.57 per week

8 **a** 12 − 3 − 4 − 5 **b** 5431
   c 5433 **d** 15 **e** 22 412 **f** 120

9 1 bag

10

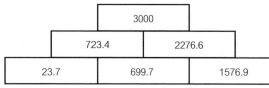

Difference = 877.2

Investigation

11 **a** 2400 **b** 1500 **c** 1800 **d** 2000
   e 40 × 50.
   f Round the number to 1 significant figure.

Reflect

12 35 × 8 = (7 × 5) × (2 × 2 × 2)
   You could write this as 7 × (2 × 2) × (2 × 5), which is 7 × 4 × 10.
   If a multiplication is difficult to work out in its current form, the factors of the numbers we are multiplying can be multiplied in any order to make the multiplication easier.

1.2 Divisibility and division

1 36

2 Multiple answers possible, e.g. 135 or 165.

3 **a** Multiple answers, e.g. 69.
   b Multiple answers, e.g. 675.
   c Multiple answers, e.g. 756.
   d Because that would be in the 10 times table, which always ends in 0, which is not one of the digits.
   e It is impossible because the sum of the digits is not divisible by 3.
   f Yes, 7 × 8 = 56 so 56 ÷ 7 = 8.
   g There were still multiple answers to each part. **d** is possible with those digits. It is still impossible to make a 5-digit number in the 3 times table.

4 **a** 3 and 4 **b** 2 and 2 **c** 2

5 **a** £6 **b** £347

6 105

7 One third, because every third multiple of 6 will be multiplied by another 3.

8 For example, 6, 12, 16, 22, 34

9 204 ÷ 15 = 13.6

10 Because it is divisible by 6 and 7, and 6 and 7 do not share factors, it must be divisible by 42, which is 6 × 7.

11 No, because 12 and 16 share factors. It must be divisible by 48 because of the common prime factors.

12 **a** Yes
   b Because factor pairs are symmetrical, as one gets larger the other gets smaller, so the square root is the point where they would both be equal.
   c Yes it is. **d** No, it is not.

13 **a** Yes **b** No
   c Yes, because the sum of the proper divisors will always be 1.

14 **a** Yes **b** Yes
   c No, because it requires a repeated factor.

Investigation

15 The answer will always be in the 13 times table if the original number was in the 13 times table.

Reflect

16 If the number is in the 6 times table, it is divisible by 3 and 2. If it is in the 9 times table, it is divisible by 3 two times. A number in the 18 times table is divisible by 2 and also by 3 two times.

1.3 Calculating with negative integers

1 **a** Negative values indicate electricity has been used from the national grid, rather than supplied to it.
   b −210 W **c** 2205 W **d** −420 W

2 **a** −24 **b** 30 **c** −210 **d** −210

3 **a** −4.2 **b** −21 **c** −33.6 **d** −3

4 **a** 6.8 **b** 20.4 **c** −5.7 **d** −5.7

5 **a** 100 **b** 50 000
   c −48 000 **d** 17 000

6 Students' own answers

7 **a** 4, −8, 16, −32, 64 **b** 24

8 Students' own calculations that give an answer of −12, e.g. 6 × −2, 10 − 22, −20 + 8, −60 ÷ 5.

9 **a** 35 °C **b** −2 °C
   c Range doesn't change.
   d Mean increases to −1.67 °C.

10 Students' own calculations that give an answer of −8, e.g. 3 × −2 − 2, −16 ÷ 2, 6 + 7 × −2.

11 −1 and −24, −2 and −12, −3 and −8, −6 and −4.

12 −8 and −4

13 Multiple answers possible, e.g. −2 and 8 or −5 and 11.

14 Students' own answers, e.g. 0.5 and −2.

15 Students' own answers, e.g. 1, −1 and 1.

Reflect

16 The answer will always be positive if there is an even number of negative numbers and will always be negative if there is an odd number of negative numbers. The answer to the example will be positive.

1.4 Powers and roots

1 **a** 41 **b** 47 **c** 30 **d** 5

2 Square numbers can only be positive; (positive)^2 = positive × positive = positive; (negative)^2 = negative × negative = positive.

3 **a** 370 **b** 400 **c** 3084 **d** 40
   e −1

4 **a** 3.5, because 11 is about halfway between 9 and 16.
   b Students' own estimates.
   c **i** 4.5 **ii** 2.2 **iii** 8.9 **iv** 9.5

5 Side of playground = $\sqrt{115} \approx \sqrt{121} = 11$.
   Side of garden $\approx \sqrt{11} \approx \sqrt{9} = 3$ m.

6 **a** $\sqrt{800} \approx \sqrt{900} = 30$ m
   b **i** No, because he rounded the side length of the plot down to 28 m and so will not have enough fencing.
   ii $4 \times \sqrt{800}$ m = 113.14 m (2 d.p.), so he should have ordered 114 m.

7 Jaya, because you can't have a negative length.

Investigation

8 a

Pyramid	1	2	3	4
Number of balls	$1^2 = 1$	$1^2 + 2^2$ $= 5$	$1^2 + 2^2 + 3^2$ $= 14$	$1^2 + 2^2 + 3^2 + 4^2$ $= 30$

  b **i** 55   **ii** 91

  c $1^2 + 2^2 + 3^2 + 4^2 + 5^2 + 6^2 + 7^2 + 8^2 + 9^2 + 10^2 +$
    $11^2 + 12^2 = 650$

9 a 4s   **b** 5s   **c** 9s

10 $5^2 = 25$ so the side length must be greater than 5 cm.

11 a Square B   **b** Square C

12 $14 + 4^2$ and $14 + (-4)^2$.
    $14 - 4^2$ and $14 - (-4)^2$.
    $25 - 2^2 - 6^2$ and $25 - 2^2 - (-6)^2$.
    $25 - (-2)^2 + 6^2$ and $25 - 2^2 + (-6)^2$.

13 Because 49 is a square number and the next square number is 64, the square root of 50 cannot be an integer.

14 a **i** True because $6 = 3 \times 2$.
    ii False because $3 + 2 \neq 3.61$ (2 d.p.).
    iii False because $3 - 1 \neq 2.24$ (2 d.p.).
    iv True because $10 \div 5 = 2$.

  b $\sqrt{144} = \sqrt{9} \times \sqrt{16}$ (other answers possible).

Reflect

15 When square rooting a measure, e.g. area of a square space to find the side length.

1.5 Powers, roots and brackets

1 a 40   **b** 50   **c** 110
  d 300   **e** 2000   **f** 600

2 a 5   **b** 7

3 a −6   **b** 105   **c** 2
  d 5   **e** 12   **f** 0

4 a 5 or −5.   **b** 4 or −4.   **c** 3 or −3.

5 a 3   **b** 10

  c $\frac{1}{2}$ **d** 1800

6 a $(5 + 4)^2 + (6 - 1)^3 = 206$
  b $(1 + 2)^2 + (6 - 5)^3 = 10$

7 a $\sqrt{3^3 + 3^2} = 6$, $13 - \left(\sqrt[3]{125} + 3\right) = 5$,
    $8 \times (11 - \sqrt[3]{1000}) = 8$, $\sqrt[3]{40 + 24} = 4$

  b Students' own calculations that give an answer of 7, e.g. $\sqrt{9} + \sqrt[3]{64}$.

8 a 15   **b** 44

9 18

10 a A 90 000 J, B 451 250 J, C 360 000 J.
  b No, it has 4 times as much energy.

11 a 27
  b Multiple answers possible, e.g. 64, 4, 4 or 8, 2, 2.

12 a The answers are the same.
  b Yes, this still gives the same answer.
  c There isn't a power of 6 that makes this work because there are different powers of 3s and 2s.

13 a The first one gives a different answer to the second two.
  b The first two give the same answer, but the second two don't. The three numbers are consecutive.
  c The three numbers are consecutive, but you get different answers. The pattern does not continue.

14 $(5 + 3)^2$

15 $(2 + 5)^3$ or $7 \times (2 + 5)^2$.

Investigation

16 This is a way to generate square numbers. It will work for consecutive odd numbers as well as consecutive even numbers.

Reflect

17 Students' own answers, e.g. calculating the cube root first as there were limited numbers it could be.

1.6 More powers, multiples and factors

1 a 2.0736   **b** 625
  c 1.856635533   **d** −0.4

2 a **i** 1, 2, 4, 8, 16
    ii 1, 2, 4, 5, 8, 10, 20, 40
    iii 1, 2, 4, 7, 8, 14, 28, 56

  b 8

3 a **i** 3, 6, 9, 12, 15, 18, 21, 24, 27, 30
    ii 4, 8, 12, 16, 20, 24, 28, 32, 36, 40
    iii 6, 12, 18, 24, 30, 36, 42, 48, 54, 60

  b 12

4 $3 \times 5 \times 11^2$

5 $20 = 2^2 \times 5$, $27 = 3^3$

6 11:00 am

7 96

8 a **i** $165 = 3 \times 5 \times 11$ **ii** $180 = 2^2 \times 3^2 \times 5$
    iii $210 = 2 \times 3 \times 5 \times 7$

  b 15   **c** 13 860

9 5

10 Multiple answers possible, e.g. 90 and 126.

11 If the other number was even, then they would also have a common prime factor of 2, so the HCF would be 30. Therefore, it must be odd.

12 $11^2 \times 13 \times 15 \times 29 \times 31^5$

Reflect

13 All numbers can be written as a product of their prime factors because the prime factors are the building blocks that form the number.

1 Extend

1 a 0   **b** 4   **c** 840

2 3

3 There are three numbers in both, but they occur closer to 200 than 300 but closer to 200 than 100.

4 414 cm²

5

1	−4	3
2	0	−2
−3	4	−1

6 81 649

7 a

Planet	Number of days to orbit the Sun	Prime factor decomposition
Mercury	88	$88 = 2^3 \times 11$
Earth	365	$365 = 5 \times 73$
Uranus	30 700	$30\,700 =$ $2^2 \times 5^2 \times 307$
Neptune	60 200	$60\,200 =$ $2^3 \times 5^2 \times 7 \times 43$

  b **i** 18 481 400   **ii** 2 241 100
    iii 675 400   **iv** 662 200

  c Uranus and Neptune   **d** 203 295 400

8 For example, 27 468 (other answers possible)

Investigation

9 This works for any two numbers and calculates the HCF every time. It works because you are finding numbers that both go into that don't have any remainder.

Investigation

10 a There are three Mersenne primes under 100.
  b Not every number calculated is a prime number.

Reflect

11 The order of operations must be considered, as well as estimating the answer to check if the final answer is sensible.

Unit 2 Area and volume

2.1 Area of a triangle

1 a 16.5 cm² **b** 12 cm² or 1200 mm²
 c 2400 mm² or 24 cm²

2 When you have used all the factor pairs of 24 as side lengths.

3 a 1 cm
 b No, we do not know either of the other two lengths, there are multiple possible triangles that have that base and perpendicular height.

4 a 5 cm²
 b i 2 cm **ii** 5 cm
 c Right-angled triangles.
 d 2 cm by 10 cm or 4 cm by 5 cm or 1 cm by 20 cm.

5 7.5 cm²

6 a 49 cm² **b** 19 cm²

7 a 24 cm² **b** 6 cm **c** 12 cm

8 a $\frac{1}{3}$
 b It does not change. The relationship between the area of the triangle and the square is proportional because the point E is defined as a proportion of the distance AD.

Reflect

9 You can only draw one square with given area. You can draw more than one triangle, using all the factor pairs of half the area for the base and height, and with different values for the other two side lengths.

2.2 Area of a parallelogram and trapezium

1 b 24 squares
 c e.g.

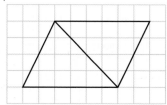

 d 12 squares
 e Area of triangle = $\frac{1}{2}$ × base × height.
  Area of parallelogram = base × height.

2 a 3 cm **b** 9.5 cm **c** 6.4 cm

3 5 × 6.4 = 32 and 8 × 4 = 32.

4 a 24x cm² **b** 4y cm²

5 a 24 cm² **b** 34 cm² **c** 2100 cm²

6 Dave is correct.
 Area of this trapezium = 10.54 cm².
 Area of trapezium with double height = 21.08 cm².
 10.54 × 2 = 21.08

7 2 cm or 20 mm.

8 a 4 cm **b** 12 cm
 c 7.5 cm and 12.5 cm.

9 36 cm²

Investigation

10 a i 30 cm² **ii** 30 cm² **iii** 30 cm²
 b There are no possible rectangles with integer side lengths.
 c There are no possible parallelograms with integer side lengths.
 d There are 7 possible trapeziums with integer side lengths.

Reflect

11 The two lengths are always perpendicular.

2.3 Volume of cubes and cuboids

1 a 60 cm²
 b Multiple answers, e.g. 1 cm by 1 cm by 60 cm, 2 cm by 6 cm by 5 cm,
  1 cm by 3 cm by 20 cm.
 c Yes
 d Yes, there are infinitely many.

2 7 cm

3 24 cm³

4 a 36 000 cm³
 b i 320 cm³ **ii** 120 cm³ **iii** 200 cm³

5 50 cm

6 a 240 cm³ **b** 168 cm³ **c** 144 cm³

7 32 bags

Investigation

8 a 512 cm³ **b** 1728 cm³
 c The volume will increase by the cube of whatever the side lengths are multiplied by.

Reflect

9 a Area is measured in square units because
  length × length = length².
 b Volume is measured in cube units because
  length × length × length = length³.

2.4 2D representations of 3D solids

1 a

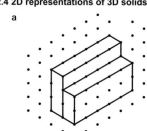

 b

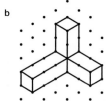

2

Plan	Front	Side

3 a i

Plan	Front	Side

ii

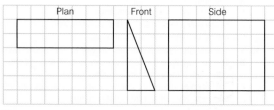

iii

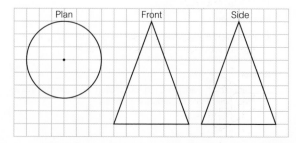

b **i** Yes
  ii No: **ii** does not show the measurement of the sloping face.

c

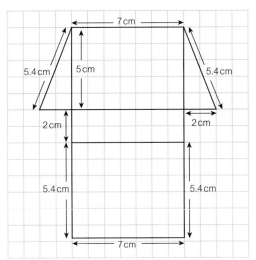

4 **a** **i**

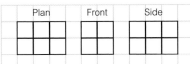

  ii

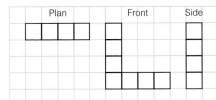

  iii

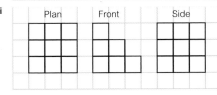

  iv

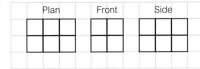

b They are the same. The solids have the same shapes when viewed from above, the front and the side.

c No

5

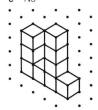

6 Students' own answers, for example, sketches of cylinder, cuboid, triangular prism, trapezoidal prism.

7

8 30 nets.

Reflect

9 **a** It does not. From the side view you cannot tell the shape of the top face (it could be a circle, square or rectangle) or the shape of the other side – it could be smaller than this.
  b A net would show you all faces.

2.5 Surface area of cubes and cuboids

1 No. Even though surface area of box < area of wrapping paper, a net of the box would not fit on the wrapping paper.

2 **a** A 6 cm by 5 cm, B 6 cm by 7 cm, C 7 cm by 5 cm.
  b $210\,cm^3$ **c** $214\,cm^2$

3 $69.24\,m^2$

4 **a** $24\,cm^2$ **b** 2 cm

5 2 cm

6 **a** A $82\,cm^2$
      B $8800\,mm^2$ (or $88\,cm^2$).
      C $62.5\,cm^2$
  b **i** Yes. The volumes will be added together.
      ii No, any faces that meet will not be counted in the surface area, so the total surface area will be less than the sum of the individual surface areas.

7 **a** $140\,cm^2$ **b** $162\,cm^2$ **c** $294\,cm^2$

8 **a** No
  b Students' own answers for example: 'Box B, because it has the least surface area for the same volume, so would need the least amount of cardboard to make, so would be cheapest.'
  c 6 cm by 6 cm by 6 cm.

Investigation

9 **a** $3202\,m^2$ **b** $520\,m^2$

Reflect

10 **a** It is not possible for two cubes to have the same volume but different surface areas because to have the same volume, the edge lengths must be the same.
  b For cuboids, they can have the same volume but different surface areas as the edge lengths do not need to be the same.

2.6 Measures

1 Football pitch 0.714 hectares, rugby pitch 1.008 hectares.

2 **a** Yes. 5.3 hectares = $53\,000\,m^2$
  b 15 625

3 192 hectares

4 **a** **i** $403.2\,cm^2$ **ii** $40\,320\,mm^2$
  b $360\,mm \times 112\,mm = 40\,320\,mm^2$.
  c Students' own answers.

5 Approximately 1 tonne.

6 **a** 90, when the possible arrangement of the quadrats within a rectangular plot is considered.
  b $\frac{1}{8}$ or 12.5%

7 No. $\frac{40}{8000} = 0.005 < \frac{5600}{1\,000\,000} = 0.0056$

8 **a** 1200 cm, 240 cm, 255 cm.
  b $73\,440\,000\,cm^3$
  c 600
  d 12–13 containers high; 3060–3315 cm high (102–110.5 ft high).
  e 21.6 tonnes (240 washing machines).

9 **a** **i** Students' own answers, e.g. 3 ft × 3 ft × 2 ft.
      ii Students' own answers, e.g. 90 cm × 90 cm × 60 cm.
  b $486\,000\,cm^3$

Reflect

10 **a** **i** g **ii** tonnes **iii** kg
  b **i** m^2 **ii** m^2 or ha **iii** cm^2
      Students' own answers.

2 Extend

1 369 cm^2

2 $\frac{5}{36}$

3 £3.52 for each 6 cm of fabric length he can cut 18 triangles, he will need 102 cm to cut 306 triangles (you have to buy fabric in straight lengths)

4 2 cm^2

5 **a** 40 cm
   b **i** 0.013 824 m^3 **ii** 1.0752 cm^2

6 32 faces are showing.

Investigation

7 Students' own answers with justification.

Investigation

8 Students' own answers based on their environment.

Reflect

9 Name the solid, describe the solids it is made from, calculate its volume, surface area, mass, draw a net, plan, elevations, isometric drawing.

Unit 3 Statistics, graphs and charts

3.1 Pie charts

1 a 36 b 9 c 6
2 a

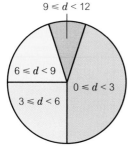

$9 \leqslant d < 12$
$6 \leqslant d < 9$
$0 \leqslant d < 3$
$3 \leqslant d < 6$

   b i   The modal distance travelled to the shops is $0 \leqslant d < 3$.
      ii Fewer than half the shoppers had travelled
          less than 3 miles.
      iii Just over 25% of shoppers had travelled
          more than 6 miles.

3 a 288 calories b 792 calories
   c 450 calories d 990 calories
4 a £40 000 b £100 000
   c Even though the band earned a greater proportion from
      CDs in 2004, the total income from CDs was greater in 2014
      – £100 000 compared with £80 000.

5 Yes, she is correct; 18 Year 8 students and 22 Year 9 students
   go home for lunch.
   (Working: $\frac{36}{360} = \frac{1}{10}$; $\frac{1}{10} \times 220 = 22$)

6 a i $\frac{2}{3}$ ii $\frac{2}{9}$
   b About 674 000 GWh.
   c About 43 000 GWh.
   d Students' own observations. For example:
      'France generates the largest proportion of its renewable
      energy through hydropower.'
      'Germany generates the largest proportion of its renewable
      energy through wind power.'

7 a Students' own answers; three sentences including, for
      example: 'The percentage of visitors going to wildlife parks
      and zoos more than doubled.'
      'The percentage going to theme parks increased slightly.'
      'The percentage visiting houses and monuments
      remained the same.'
      'The percentage visiting museums and gardens fell by
      about a quarter.'
   b Although the percentage is larger in 1981, this might
      represent fewer people than in 1999 (i.e. if the overall visitor
      numbers were higher in 1999); we are not told how many
      people each pie chart represents, so we cannot work out
      the numbers of visitors to compare them.
8 a School B b School A c 360
   d School A
   e School A

Reflect

9 Francesca can only know the numbers of students taking
   history if she knows the numbers of students in each school.
   Without this information, she can only compare the proportions
   of students taking history.

3.2 Using tables

1 a

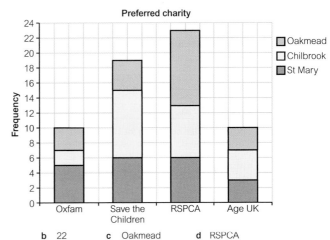

Preferred charity

Legend: Oakmead, Chilbrook, St Mary

   b 22   c Oakmead   d RSPCA
2 Students' own answers, for example:

	Margherita	Pepperoni	Four cheese	Total
9"				
12"				
Total				

3 a Mean 4.45, median 5, mode 5.
   b The median, because it is the half-way point and
      agrees with the mode.
   c Students' own answers, for example: 'Using the table,
      because I did not have to add up individual numbers.'

4 a

	$135 \leqslant h < 140$	$140 \leqslant h < 145$	$145 \leqslant h < 150$	$150 \leqslant h < 155$	$155 \leqslant h < 160$	Total
Boys	3	7	3	4	0	17
Girls	2	2	6	4	1	15
Total	5	9	9	8	1	32

   b 10
   c 18
   d $\frac{9}{16}$
5 a Students' own grouped frequency tables. For example:

Minutes late, m	Frequency
$0 \leqslant m < 5$	8
$5 \leqslant m < 10$	1
$10 \leqslant m < 15$	4
$15 \leqslant m < 20$	2
$20 \leqslant m < 25$	1
$m \geqslant 25$	2

   b Students' own answers. For example:
      'The modal class is $0 \leqslant m < 5$, but this doesn't mean most
      trains were less than 5 minutes late.'
      'Very few trains were more than 20 minutes late.'

Investigation

6 a Students' own answers
   b Students' own answers
   c Students' choices
   d Students justify their choice above, for example: '10 class
      intervals is too many because there are not enough pieces
      of data in each class.'

7 a Mean 19.9, median 20, there are 4 modes 12, 19, 23 and 30

b The median, because it shows that 50% of pupils did better and 50% did worse than that.

c There are not many repeated values, so an ungrouped table would be nearly as long as the raw list.

d

Marks (m)	Frequency
$0 \leqslant m < 10$	2
$10 \leqslant m < 15$	7
$15 \leqslant m < 20$	6
$20 \leqslant m < 25$	7
$25 \leqslant m \leqslant 30$	9

e Because you are comparing the proportion of the marks they got. If you just compare the scores, it might look like they did better even if they did worse.

f

Percentage (p)	Frequency
$0 \leqslant p < 10$	0
$10 \leqslant p < 20$	1
$20 \leqslant p < 30$	1
$30 \leqslant p < 40$	1
$40 \leqslant p < 50$	6
$50 \leqslant p < 60$	2
$60 \leqslant p < 70$	6
$70 \leqslant p < 80$	3
$80 \leqslant p < 90$	4
$90 \leqslant p \leqslant 100$	7

g They did better on the first test because there were more students between 90% and 100% than on the second test.

h Students' own diagrams and conclusions.

Reflect

8 a Students' own answers, for example: 'The diagram was more useful because it was easier to see the shape of the pattern.'

b Students' own answers, for example: 'I chose a bar chart so I could see where the most marks were.'

3.3 Stem and leaf diagrams

1 a 37 **b** 41 **c** 34

d The mode

2 a Before video: median 26, range 36.

b Students' own answers, for example: 'The median for before watching the video was lower than the median for after watching the video'. 'The range for before watching the video was lower than the range for after watching the video'. After video: median 37, range 38.

3 a

```
1 | 2 2 3 4 4 6 7 9    Key
2 | 0 2                1 | 2 means 12
```

b There is not a large range of stems, so it is not much different to just an ordered list of the data.

4 a Mean 14.8, median 13; mean is higher.

b Mean 24.8, median 23; mean is higher.

c Mean 29.5, median 32; median is higher.

5 Students' own answers, for example:

```
0 | 1
1 | 0 0 0
2 | 0 0 0 9
3 | 9 9 9 9    Key
4 | 9 9 9      4 | 9 means 49
```

6 Students' own answers, for example:

```
0 | 1 2 3
1 | 0 7
2 | 1 2      Key
3 | 0 0      2 | 1 means 21
```

7 Students' own answers, for example:

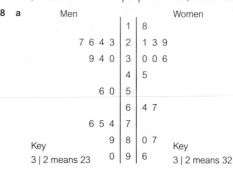

```
          3 2 | 0 | 1 4
        3 3 2 | 1 | 1 4 5
Key     7 5 0 | 2 | 1 3 6  Key
1 | 3 means 31   4 1 | 3 | 2 3   3 | 2 means 32
```

8 a

```
        Men              Women
                | 1 | 8
        7 6 4 3 | 2 | 1 3 9
          9 4 0 | 3 | 0 0 6
                | 4 | 5
            6 0 | 5 |
                | 6 | 4 7
          6 5 4 | 7 |
Key             9 | 8 | 0 7    Key
3 | 2 means 23  0 | 9 | 6      3 | 2 means 32
```

b

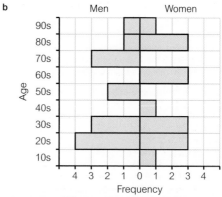

c The stem and leaf gives more information and is better to find the mean from, but the population pyramid shows the modal class better.

d The men are generally younger than the women. The women are either older or younger: there are fewer women with an age in the middle. The oldest people are more likely to be women.

9 a

```
0 | 3 3 4 4 5 8
1 | 0 1 2 3 3 4
2 | 2 3
3 | 0            Key
4 | 3            2 | 3 means 23
```

b

Number of birds	Frequency
0–9	6
10–19	6
20–29	2
30–39	1
40–49	1

c

Birds seen each day

d They are the same shape.

Investigation

10 a

Multiples of 3		Prime Numbers
9 6 3	0	2 3 5 7
8 5 2	1	1 3 7 9
7 4 1	2	3 9
9 6 3 0	3	1 7
8 5 2	4	1 3 7
7 4 1	5	3 9
9 6 3 0	6	1 7
8 5 2	7	1 3 9
7 4 1	8	3 9
9 6 3 0	9	7

Key
8 | 1 means 18

Key
3 | 1 means 31

b There are more prime numbers between 0 and 20 than multiples of 3.

c Students' own answers, for example: 'The closer to 100 you get, the fewer prime numbers'; 'Every three rows there are four multiples of 3 rather than 3.'

Reflect

11 It is easier to find the modal class from a bar chart. It is easier to find the median and mode from a stem and leaf diagram. They both show the shape of the data distribution clearly.

3.4 Comparing data

1 The dog has the biggest range of values, so is the least consistent, while the plane has the smallest range and is the most consistent. The helicopter has the highest median so it can travel furthest on average.

2 a 15 minutes, 4.25 seconds.

b Men's mean time of 13:43.57 is less than mean time for women time of 15:09.10. The men were faster, on average. Men's range is 3.71 seconds, which is smaller than the women's 13.63 seconds – the men's times were all closer together, and less varied.

3 Students' own answers. For example: 'The snow at Winter Park was less deep than at Avioraz from December to March. The snow at Avioraz started to melt first. Avioraz had much deeper snow than Winter Park.'

4 a,b

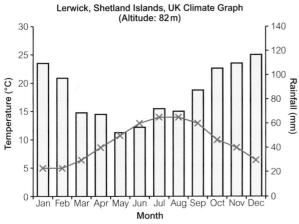

Lerwick, Shetland Islands, UK Climate Graph (Altitude: 82 m)

c The maximum temperature increased steadily between March and July, then began to decrease between September and December.
The rainfall decreased between January and May, then began to increase again between June and December.

5 a 27 million.

b 110 million.

c The scales for full-time and part-time workers are different, so they aren't comparable.

d No, because the scales are different.

Reflect

6 Need the range, so we could see which student's score was most consistent.

3.5 Scatter graphs

1 a Positive correlation   **b** 8 m

c 25 cm and 32 cm

d (41, 16), because the point lies well away from all the other points on the graph.

e Students' own answers, for example: it could be a different species of tree.

2 a

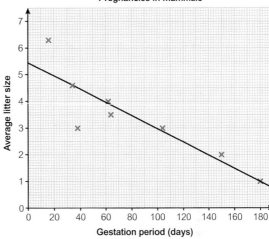

Pregnancies in mammals

b (Weak) negative correlation

c Mammals with longer gestation periods tend to have fewer offspring in each litter.
OR
Mammals with shorter gestation periods tend to have more offspring in each litter.

3 a,c

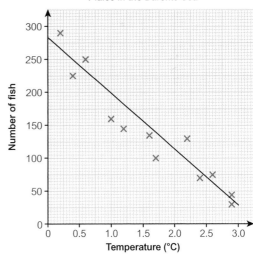

Plaice in the Barents Sea

b Weak negative correlation

d The population of plaice in the Barents Sea could decrease if the temperature of the sea rises.

4　**a**　Negative correlation
　　b　Designer Tshirts has no correlation and TshirtsRus has negative correlation.

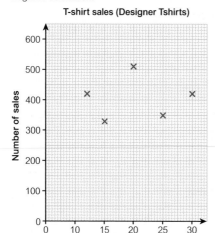

T-shirt sales (Designer Tshirts)

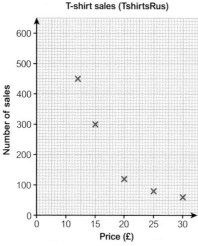

T-shirt sales (TshirtsRus)

5　**a**　No correlation
　　b

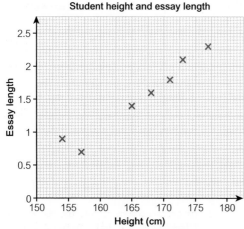

Student height and essay length

　　c　There is positive correlation. It must be a coincidence as there should be no relationship between height and length of essay.

Investigation

6　**a**　Students' own graphs.
　　b　Positive correlation.
　　c　No. People usually have thumbs and fingers in proportion to each other. It is unusual to have very large thumbs but small fingers, and vice versa.

Reflect

7　No, it does not. It is likely that the high amount of crime causes more police to be hired. Just because there is correlation does not mean that increasing one variable will increase the other.

3.6　Misleading graphs

1　**a**　The scales on the sales axes are different. The scale for tablet sales starts at 0 and goes up in intervals of 1 million. The scale for PC sales has a discontinuity between 0 and 30 and goes up in intervals of 2 million.
　　b

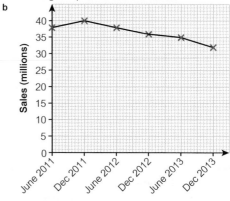

　　c　Students' own answers. For example: 'Tablet sales increase by more than 4 times in 2 years'.

2　**a**　The scale on the vertical axis has unequal intervals. Bars for 2017 and 2018 are wider.
　　b

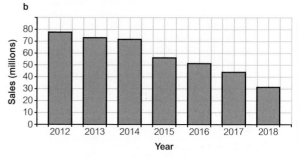

3　**a**　Students' own graphs, for example:

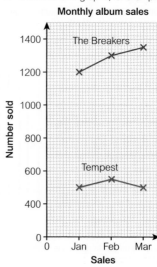

Monthly album sales

b

Monthly album sales

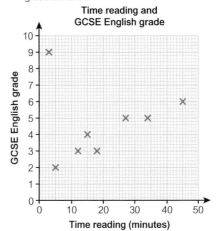

4 a Positive correlation.
   b As the temperature increases, the length of the bar increases.
   c Because there are lots of values that are not used.
   d No, because there is still strong correlation shown.

5 a–c

Dungeness crab growth

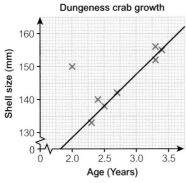

b Strong positive correlation

Reflect

6 Check that the scale goes up in equal steps. Check that graphs being compared have the same scale. Check that bars on a bar graph are the same width.

Extend

1

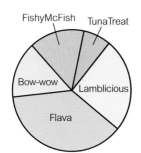

2 a

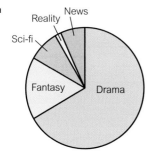

---

b

Favourite type of TV show

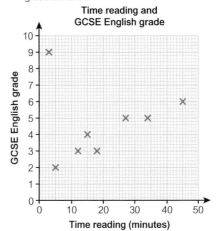

c Students' own answers, for example: the bar chart shows the actual numbers of people more clearly, but the pie chart shows the proportions more clearly.

3 a The value for the person who reads for 3 minutes.
   b This is best shown with a scatter diagram as it shows the relationship between two sets of data.
   c The school should show this because, apart from the 3 minute reader, it shows positive correlation between the amount of time students read and GCSE English grade achieved.

Time reading and GCSE English grade

4 a Allison   **b** Charlotte

Number of flowers grown

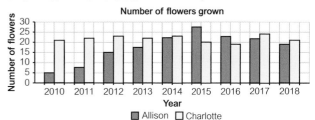

5 Students' own answers, for example:

```
0 | 3 3 3 4
1 | 6 7 8
2 | 2 3        Key
3 | 1          2 | 3 means 23
```

6 a Yes, because there is only one answer.
   b No, we only know what the two missing data points must sum to.

7 4

Investigation

8 Students' own answers, for example:

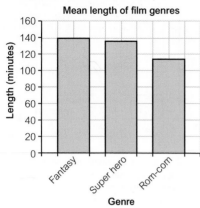

The graph shows the mean runing time of each genre. Fantasy movies and super hero movies run for almost the same length of time on average, while rom-coms are roughly 20 minutes shorter on average.

Reflect

9 Students' own answers.

Unit 4 Expressions and equations

4.1 Algebraic powers

1　a　$3x$　　　b　x^3 and $27x^3$
　　c　$28x^3$　　d　$28\,000\,cm^3$

2　a　$a - 2, a, a + 2, 2a, a^2, 2a^2, (2a)^2, a^3$
　　b　$a - 2, a^3, a^2, a\ 2a^2, (2a)^2, 2a, a + 2$
　　c　We do not know the value of b so we cannot work out the value of ab.

3　a　The answer is always the original number.
　　b　$x, 2x, 4x^2, x^2, x$

4　Yes, because $(3y)^2$ is the same as $9y^2$ which will always be larger than $3y^2$ for $y \neq 0$.

5　Sometimes true, for example, if $x = 0$, but not true for most values of x as usually $2x^2 \neq x^4$.

6　a　$2x^2$　　　b　$6x$　　　c　$6x^3$

7　a　$3x$
　　b

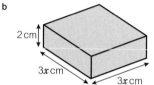

　　c　$6x + 2$
　　d　$54x^2$

8　a　$6x^2$, where x is the width.
　　b　$2x^2$
　　c　$2.1\,m \times 2.1\,m \times 4.2\,m$

9　a　y^2　　　b　x^2y^2　　　c　$4xy$
　　d　i　x^2y^2　　ii　$5xy$
　　　　iii　Yes, the rectangle will have larger perimeter because $5xy > 4xy$.

Investigation

10　$x = 4$

Reflect

11　a　i　Sometimes　　ii　When $x = 0$
　　b　i　Sometimes　　ii　When $x = 0$
　　c　i　Sometimes　　ii　When $x = 0$
　　d　i　Sometimes　　ii　When $a = 0, a = 1$ or $b = 0$

4.2 Expressions and brackets

1　a　$v - 50$　　　　b　$8(v - 50)$
　　c　$2000 - 8(v - 50)$　　d　$2400 - 8v$
　　e　$400\,ml$

2　a　$7x + 7$　　b　$2m - 23$　　c　12
　　d　$12 - x$　　e　$8x + 6$　　f　$6x - 17$

3　a　$8(x + 3)$ or $8x + 24$
　　b　$5(x - 2)$ or $5x - 10$
　　c　$3x + 34$

4　a　i　$x(3x + 2)$　　ii　$3x^2 + 2x$
　　b　i　$2y(5 + 3y)$　　ii　$10y + 6y^2$
　　c　i　$10z(3z - 7)$　　ii　$30z^2 - 70z$

5　a　$250x$
　　b　The water would be deeper than the swimming pool, which is impossible.
　　c　$500x$

6　a　$x^3 + 4x^2$　　b　225
　　c　$2 \times x \times x + 4 \times x(x + 4) = 2x^2 + 4x^2 + 16x = 6x^2 + 16x$
　　d　No

7　a, b　A　$15a + 5b$　　B　$18a + 2b$
　　c　A　35　　B　50
　　d　No, because one of the side lengths would be negative.

8　$\dfrac{5(2x + 2)}{2}$ or $5x + 5$

9　a　$4x(3x + 2)$ or $12x^2 + 8x$.
　　b　$2x^2 + \dfrac{4x}{3}$
　　c　$80\,cm^2$　　d　It is a square.

10　$t(m + 20)$, where t is time in minutes and m is miles.

Reflect

11　a　No
　　b　Students' own answers, for example 'Not necessarily, although in some formulae letters are often chosen to represent a quantity starting with that letter, which makes the formula easier to remember.'

4.3 Factorising expressions

1　a　x^2　　　b　p　　　c　y^2
　　d　$4z$　　　e　$5m^3$　　f　pq

2　a　$5x(x + 3) = 5x^2 + 15x$
　　b　$3y(2y - 4) = 6y^2 - 12y$

3　Students' own answers, for example
　　$12x^2 + 24x, 12x(2x - 4 - x + 6), 12x(x + 4) - 24x$

4　a　3 and $4x^2 + 6$, 2 and $6x^2 + 9$, 6 and $2x^2 + 3$
　　b　6 and $2x^2 + 3$. The full factorisation is $6(2x^2 + 3)$.
　　c　254

5　$3ab + a = a(3b + 1)$, $3ab + a + ab^2 = a(3b + 1 + b^2)$,
　　$3ab + a^2b - b^3 = b(3a + a^2 - b^2)$

6　a　x and $5x^2 + 2$
　　b　No; there is only one possible factorisation. The only common factor is x.

7　There is no common factor between the two terms.

8　Sides are $x\,m$ and $(x + 4)\,m$, and $(x + 4)\,m$ is $4\,m$ longer than x.

9

$5x$	$(x + 2)$	$5x^2 + 10x$
$2x^2 - 5x$	3	$6x^2 - 15x$
$10x^3 - 25x^2$	$3x + 6$	

10　$1\,m$ and $3\,m$

11　$8n^2 + 8 = 8(n^2 + 1)$, which is 8 multiplied by an integer, so must be a multiple of 8.

12　a　$6xy$
　　b　Multiple answers are possible, for example, $6xy + 12xy$, $6xy + 24xy$, $6xy + 30xy$.
　　c　Then there would be another common factor of 2, i.e. 4 would be a common factor.

13　a　$3x$　　　b　0.5

14　$6x(x + 4)$

15　$10x^2 - 2x, 9x^2 - 2x + x^2, 9x^2 - x + x^2 - x$.

16　a　10　　　b　$5(x + 1) = 5 \times 11 = 5(10 + 1)$
　　c　105　　　d　143

Reflect

17　Yes, because factorisation is the inverse of expanding brackets.

4.4 One-step equations

1　a

$$3w$$

　　b　Length $= 9\,cm$, width $= 3\,cm$

2　a　$9n$
　　b　$12 = 9n$, so $n = 1\frac{1}{3}$ hours
　　c　2 hours 40 minutes

3　$2A + 3C = 28$
　　$2 \times 2C + 3C = 7C = 28$
　　$C = £4$
　　$A = 2C$ so $A = £8$

4　a　$3x + x = 1, x = 0.25$
　　b　15

5　a　$x - 15 = 9\,cm$
　　b　$24\,cm$
　　c　$6x + 2x = 24$
　　　　$8x = 24$
　　　　$x = 3$
　　　　Longest side $= 9\,cm$

6　a　i　$9.25h = 92.50$　　ii　$h = 10$
　　b　i　$12 \times 9.25 = 10 \times 3w$　　ii　$w = £3.70$

7 £1620 = 120 × h

h = £13.50

8 12

9 a $x ÷ 5 = 12 × 50$ **b** 3000

10 a 8 **b** 6 **c** 5

11 a $x + 5x = 378$

b 315 **c** $5x = 60$ **d** 72

e It is not.

Investigation

12 Their father was 22.

Reflect

13 An equation shows that two mathematical expressions are equal and can be solved to find the value of an unknown variable, while a formula shows a relationship between two or more variables.

4.5 Two-step equations

1 a $x = 4$ **b** $x = 4$ **c** $x = 2$

   d $x = 6$ **e** $x = 5$ **f** $x = 0.5$

   g $x = 2.5$ **h** $x = -0.25$

2 a $x = 4$ **b** $x = 10$ **c** $x = -2$

3 a $-\frac{5}{7}$ **b** -1 **c** $\frac{5}{7}$

4 a -2 **b** -2 **c** -6

   d $-\frac{2}{3}$ **e** $\frac{2}{9}$ **f** $-\frac{2}{9}$

5 a $3x - 5 = 31$ **b** £12

6 a $x = 5$

   b The piece of card is 4 cm by 10 cm and the hole is 2 cm by 8 cm.

7 a 1 **b** $x = 0.12$

8 a 196, 197, 198 **b** $3n = 591$, $n = 197$

   c 196, 197, 198 **d** Equation

9 a $2a + 1 = 7.30$, where a is the price of a sandwich.

   b €3.15 **c** €2.15

Investigation

10 Infinitely many possible equations, for example, $2x + 1 = \frac{13}{7}$. Substitute in the value of x to check.

Reflect

11 No: they can be fractions, decimals or negative integers. Q2c finds a negative value of x and the solution to the equation in Q7 is a decimal value less than 1.

4.6 The balancing method

1 a $2n + 9 = 25$, $n = 8$

   b $2(n + 9) = 25$, $n = 3.5$

   c Subtraction and division. Both use inverse operations 'subtract 9' and 'divide by 2'. The order of inverse operations was different in both.

2 a $24x^2 - 5x^3$

   b i 19 cm³ **ii** 56 cm³

      iii 81 cm³ **iv** 64 cm³

   c When $x = 5$, the difference is negative, which cannot be true for a volume.

3 a $v = 11$ **b** $x = 4$ **c** $w = 80$

   d $h = 3$ **e** $a = 4.5$ **f** $u = 5$

4 a £23.75 **b** 1.7 minutes **c** 0.25 miles

   d i £26 **ii** $\frac{2}{3}$ miles **iii** 6.2 minutes

5 £18.06

6 15 g for Pickle and 45 g for Mango

7 a $0.60 + 30R = 1.80$, where R is the cost of 1 red bead, £0.04

   b £3.60

   c 6 black beads, 9 red beads.

8 50p

9 $x = 6$ cm

Investigation

10 Infinitely many possible answers. Should all be able to be solved so that $x = 18$.

Reflect

11 $3x - 7 = 12$: add then divide

   $3(x - 7) = 12$: divide then add

   The inverse operations are in the reverse order to the operations in the equation so, for example, when the equation has multiply then subtract, you add and then divide.

4 Extend

1 The answer will be $10x + 20$, so you need to subtract 20 then divide by 10 and you will have the original number.

2 $9x + 18 = 9(x + 2)$

3 $3x(x + 2)$ or $3x^2 + 6x$

4 $3x + 4x + 5x = 180$

        $x = 15$

   None of the angles are 90°.

5 7 cm, 12 cm, 7 cm, 24 cm

6 Multiple answers possible, for example, $3w + (-4)$, $-2x + 6$, $2y + (-2)$.

7 64 cm

8 891.5 cm (1 d.p.)

9 $x = 4$

10 2 187 cm³

$x + 1$	$x - 4$	$x + 3$
$x + 2$	x	$x - 2$
$x - 3$	$x + 4$	$x - 1$

11 $x = 6$

12 384 cm²

Investigation

13 Multiple answers for each number. All numbers from 1 to 10 are possible.

Investigation

14 It is true. $x + x + a + x + 2a = 3x + 3a = 3(x + a)$

Reflect

15 Students' own answers, for example: 'When looking at changing the numbers, I have been able to see more clearly where each number is used and saved time.'

Unit 5 Real-life graphs

5.1 Conversion graphs

1 a Approximately 124%
   b Chelsea's hair, by 112.5%.

2 a No, he needs more butter and sugar.
   b He is correct, because the amount of sugar is directly proportional to the number of cups.
   c Julia has converted from cups to grams instead of grams to cups.

3 a It would go through the origin, because if there are $0\,cm^3$ there would also be 0 litres.
   b 7 litres is greater because it is $7000\,cm^3$.

4 a

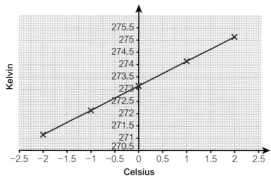

Conversion between Kelvin and Celsius

   b 0 degrees Kelvin is not the same as 0 degrees Celsius, which is possible because temperatures can be negative.
   c 373.15 Kelvin

5 a 1 kroner = 0.10 euro   b Germany

6 a Even without studying just before the exam, you would expect students to be able to answer some questions.
   b If you study for 100 hours, you would not expect to do 10 times better than if you studied for 10 hours. There is also a maximum number of marks.
   c 16
   d Most of these are very close to what the model predicts, except for the 0 hours which might be an anomaly, so it is a good model.

Reflect

7 They have the same number of extra units for each additional unit so will always make a straight line. They will always pass through the origin because if you have no money in one currency, you also have no money in the other currency.

   The conversion graph between Celsius and Kelvin does not pass through the origin because 0 °C is not the same as 0 °K.

5.2 Distance–time graphs

1

Section	Distance (miles)	Time taken	Speed (miles per hour)
A	25 – 0 = 25	30 minutes	50
B	60 – 25 = 35	30 minutes	70
C	180 – 60 = 120	2 hours	60
D	190 – 180 = 10	15 minutes	40
E	205 – 190 = 15	45 minutes	20

2 a Sania – the time to get to the friend's house is the same as the time to get home.
      Karl – the time at the friend's house is not long enough.
   b

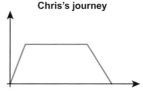

Chris's journey

3 a 26.7 mph
   b

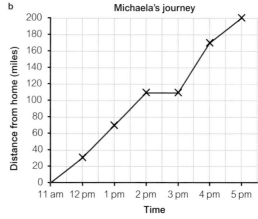

Michaela's journey

   c 2 pm–3 pm
   d 3 pm–4 pm
   e She was not moving at 26.7 mph for the whole three hours, as she was stationary between 2 pm and 3 pm.

4 a 42 km
   b 9.45 am
   c A: 2.75 h B: 2.25 h C: 3.25 h, therefore Athlete B.
   d i Around 11.22 am
      ii 21.5 km
   e No; they are likely to slow down towards the end of the race; they are likely to run slower going uphill, etc.

5 a i C   ii A   iii B
   b D The runner starts off quickly, stops for a while and then runs quickly to the finish.
      E The runner starts off slowly, then runs quickly and then runs slowly again to the finish.

Investigation

6 a Students' own distance–time graphs and roller coasters.
   b The length of the graph would get shorter, because a smaller number of hours would pass compared with the number of seconds.
   c The graph will never show a loop because that would mean the roller coaster is going backwards in time.

Reflect

7 a It would mean that the distance had two different values for the same time, which is not possible.
   b This would show that the distance had changed without any time passing.

5.3 Line graphs

1 a

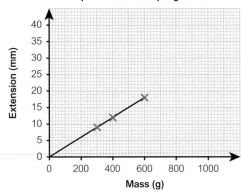

Graph of mass and spring extension

(y-axis: Extension (mm), 0 to 40; x-axis: Mass (g), 0 to 1000)

b Yes
c 10.45 mm
d 36 mm
e No

2 a

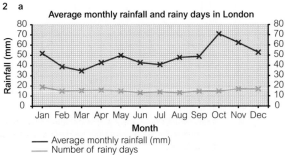

Average monthly rainfall and rainy days in London

(left y-axis: Rainfall (mm), 0–80; right y-axis: Number of days, 0–80; x-axis: Month, Jan–Dec)

— Average monthly rainfall (mm)
— Number of rainy days

b March and February   **c** September

3 a 50%

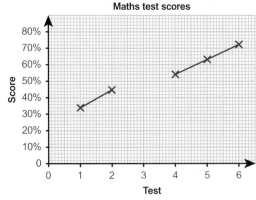

Maths test scores

(y-axis: Score, 0–80%; x-axis: Test, 0–6)

b Ursel is likely to not have scored 0, so using a 0 will make the average percentage look worse than it is.
c The data for Maths has nothing to do with the data for English.
d Students' own answers, for example 'No, because they could be very different tests in the next academic year.'

4 a 94th
b Yes, because the downward trend is accelerating.
c It looks like the graph is now starting to trend upward, so it is likely the author's book will not reach the top 10.

5 a 69 mph
b Fairly accurate as speed was measured every 12 minutes.
c Less accurate because speed could vary a lot in 1.2 hour gaps.

Reflect

6 a 350 g is between two places we have values for, but we do not know the actual value for 350 g.
b 350 g is likely to be more accurate than 1200 g because 350 g lies between two values we know, whereas 1000 g lies beyond the graph of values we know.

5.4 More line graphs

1 a The share price increased.
b $11
c 1 September, 1 November
d 1 July, 1 October
e $480
f Yes, if you did not buy them in July 2013, as you will make a profit. It might be risky to keep the shares beyond then.

2 a £200 000
b £500 000
c 2009, 2013, 2014, 2016, 2017, 2018
d 2012
e i Income decreased.   ii Income increased.
f It is hard to predict as the graph goes up and down.

3 a It does not go up in equal amounts; it multiplies by 10 each time.
b

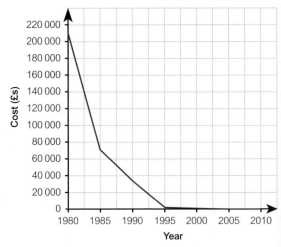

Cost of 1 GB of data storage

(y-axis: Cost (£s), 0 to 220 000; x-axis: Year, 1980 to 2010)

c It decreased (rapidly).
d The second graph because it shows the quick decrease in prices.

Investigation

4 Georgia should invest in Chloe's Cones because as time is going on, Chloe's Cones is making more sales, but Ian's Ices is making fewer sales. Georgia should expect to get around £170 per year, so it would take 4 years for Georgia to get the £600 back.

Reflect

5 The increase in the first few months is much steadier than the overall increase.

5.5 Real-life graphs

1 a 1   **b** 3
c 4   **d** 2

2 a 1
b A = 1, B = 2

3 a ≈ 52%
b ≈ 3%
c Between 1995 and 2000
d The percentage increased.
e 65%

4 a i 30%
    ii 20%
b The percentage of the population aged 0–14 decreased.
c 40–64 and 65+
d Older. The percentage of the population aged 40+ is increasing and the percentage aged 0–39 is decreasing.

5 Students' own answers, for example:

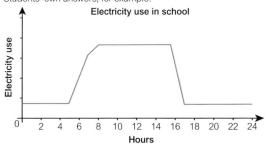

Electricity use in school

Investigation

6 The overall trend is increasing. The women in Somalia can expect to live longer than the men and their life expectancy is increasing at a greater rate.

Reflect

7 No, because you would have had to compare all of the numbers. On the graph you can clearly see the trend without having to compare individual numbers.

5.6 Curved graphs

1 a

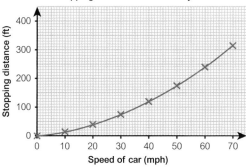

Stopping distance of a car in dry weather

b 206 feet (± 3 feet)
c Approximately 12 mph
d 35 feet
e No; for example, it will be further in rain and even further in snow, as both conditions stop the tyres gripping the road so well.

2 a i C   **ii** A   **iii** B
b About 60 m; the graph is not so steep, showing that his speed of falling slows.
c 3 seconds; for example, it takes 6 seconds (7 to 13 seconds on the graph) to drop 40 m (60 to 20 m on the graph), half of 40 m is 20 m and half of 6 seconds is 3 seconds.
d 16 seconds; for example, he has another 20 m to drop, so another 3 seconds on the graph is 13 + 3 = 16 seconds; OR if you extend the line of the graph, it gets to 0 m at 16 seconds.

3 a A = 2, B = 3, C = 4
b

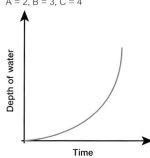

4 a

Dropped from	2 m
1st bounce	0.6 × 2 = 1.2 m
2nd bounce	0.6 × 1.2 = 0.72 m
3rd bounce	0.6 × 0.72 = 0.43 m
4th bounce	0.6 × 0.432 = 0.26 m

b

Number of bounces	0	1	2	3	4
Height (m)	10	8	6.4	5.12	4.096

5 a

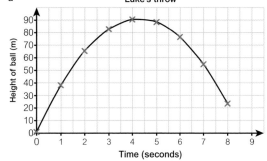

Luke's throw

b No: it is not a linear graph.
c Because Luke's arm is 1 m above the ground when he throws the ball.
d Approximately 1.4 seconds and 7.2 seconds
e One is on the way up, the other is on the way down.
f ≈ 8.6 seconds

Reflect

6 a The container does not fill at a constant rate. When the dish is narrow (at the bottom) it fills faster than when it is wider (at the top).
b Similar because the curve starts off steeply, and then becomes less steep (as the ball slows down). Different because the curve for the ball curves back downwards as it begins to fall, whereas the curve for the container ends when the container is full.

5 Extend

1 a decreases
b ≈ 65 N/cm²
c No
d You cannot apply a force on an area of 0 cm².
e i They will mark the floor because a large force goes through a small area (the heel).
    ii A sharp knife has a smaller area so the same force will generate a higher pressure.
    iii They exert a large force through a small area – their toes.

2 a 64
b–d

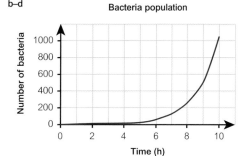

Bacteria population

e i 100
    ii 375

3 a

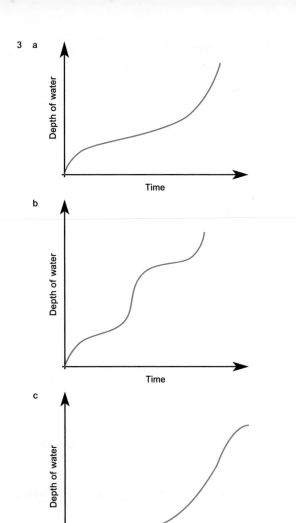

b

c

d

Investigation

6 a

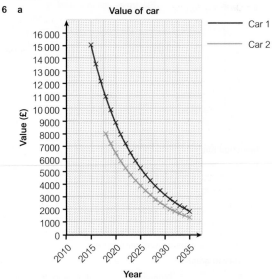

Value of car

Car 1
Car 2

b The second car will always be worth less than the first, but the difference between their values gets smaller over time.

c Neither of the cars will ever be worth £0.

d The problem is that the values of the cars are not likely to decrease at the same rate every year. There are lots of other factors affecting the value of a car. The value of the whole car will reach £0 in the real world, but can be sold for parts.

Reflect

7 It is easier to see trends in the data in a graph. A table is more useful for seeing the numbers and calculating averages, for example.

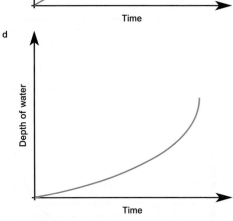

4 a 3.9 minutes

b Because no points were recorded that high. The data is only recorded every half minute.

c The amount of time the egg is boiled for cannot be negative and the score is from 0 to 5.

d There should be a point where the egg is close to perfect then it decreases in quality. The length of time an egg is boiled for does not make it better beyond a certain point.

5 a 75 counts per second

b 42 days

c 27 days

d No, it reduces to very close to 0 but will never actually reach it.

Unit 6 Decimals and ratio

6.1 Ordering decimals and rounding

1 a

River basin	Drainage area (million km^2)
Nile	3.3
Amazon	6.1
Yangtze	1.7
Mississippi	3.2
Yenisei	2.6

River basin	Drainage area (million km^2)
Yellow River	0.9
Ob	3.0
Paraná	2.6
Congo	3.7
Amur	1.9

b

River basin	Drainage area (million km^2)
Nile	3
Amazon	6
Yangtze	2
Mississippi	3
Yenisei	3

River basin	Drainage area (million km^2)
Yellow River	0.9
Ob	3
Paraná	3
Congo	4
Amur	2

  c Rounding to 1 d.p.
  d Some of the areas in the table are probably rounded values, such as the Yellow River, Ob and Congo, because they all end with multiple 0s.

2 a 0.3405, 0.345, 0.3405, 0.3504
  b 0.34, 0.35, 0.35, 0.34; no, it is not still possible because some of the numbers are now the same.
  c 0.3, 0.4, 0.4, 0.3; no, had to use the original numbers or they would round differently.

3 Students' own answers, for example,
  a 3.221 **b** 2.541 **c** 2.461
  d 3.247 **e** 3.253

4 a Area = 9.1035 m^2, perimeter = 12.24 m
  b 4 m and 3 m
  c Area = 12 m^2, perimeter = 14 m
  d It is an overestimate because both numbers were rounded up.
  e The area and perimeter are almost the same, but when rounded to 1 significant figure they rounded down and the rounded area and perimeter were much smaller.

5 a 2 800 000
  b **i** 2.9 million **ii** 0.19 million **iii** $\frac{1}{15}$

6 a Barry
  b Any number between 7.5 and 8 (not including 8 itself).

7 a £213.72 **b** £13
  c Because it rounds down to £20.
  d No. You need to know the individual amounts to know how each one rounded in order to work out how much she saves.
  e Students' own answers, for example, it is not a good idea, because most of Hafsa's expenses may round down and she will underestimate how much she spent and not put much money in savings.

8 a More than 5 g
  b There could be, because 25 × 6 = 150.

Reflect

9 a Students' own answers, for example measuring medicine doses.
  b Students' own answers, for example communicating very large numbers in a news headline.
  c It doesn't matter if you round using decimal places or significant figures, but you need to be aware of the impact on accuracy.

6.2 Place-value calculations

1 a 54 940 **b** 5.494 **c** 82
2 a 6.2 × 0.000 01 **b** 3.58 × 0.000 001
  c 9.8 × 0.000 000 0001
3 a 135
  b 135. You get the same answer.
  c 0.35 × 450

4 0.01
5 You are asking for less than one lot of the number, so it will be smaller than one lot of the number i.e., the original number.
6 a 11 **b** 1100 **c** 1100 **d** 1001
  e Students' own answers, for example,
    (123 + 1230) ÷ 123 = 11
    (123 + 12 300) ÷ 123 = 101
7 Students' own answers, for example

×	0.2	0.1
0.3	*A*	*B*
0.4	*C*	*D*

8 Students' own answers, for example 0.7 and 0.5.
9 a 24.5
  b 4 is a factor of 980, because 98 ÷ 4 = 24.5, so 980 ÷ 4 = 245, which is an integer.
  c 4 is a factor of 1180, because 118 ÷ 4 = 29.5, so 1180 ÷ 4 = 295, which is an integer.
  d No, but it is a factor of 14 600.
10 A = 1, B = 8, C = 3
11 a Two
  b Students' own answers, for example: 1.3 × 3.1 = 4.03, 2.4 × 4.2 = 10.08
  c *G* = 7, *H* = 9
12 Students' own answers, for example 3.15 and 3.7.

Investigation

13 a 1, 10, 11, 100, 101, 110, 111, 1000, 1001, 1010.
  b The calculation is 4 × 5 = 20.
  c Students' own answers for other calculations, for example 100 × 1.01 = 101.00 (check: 4 × 1.25 = 5).

Reflect

14 Students' own answers, for example, 'I used the fact that multiplication was an inverse of division to write a division.'

6.3 Calculations with decimals

1

×	0.001	0.2	1.001
7	0.007	1.4	7.007
6	0.006	1.2	6.006
0.001	0.000 001	0.0002	0.001 001
8.09	0.008 09	1.618	8.098 09
9.08	0.009 08	1.816	9.089 08

2 a 0.032 **b** 0.79 **c** 1.674 **d** 36.25
3 3982.75 m^2
4 a £1082.15 **b** £108.22
  c Bike from Bike Shop, £40.37 cheaper.
5 USA 1.59 UKs, Greenland 3.53 UKs, Australia 2.06 UKs, France 0.27 UKs.
6 4 cm
7 Multiple answers, for example 8 and 7.084.
8 a 0.2 cm **b** 0.4 cm

Investigation

9 Yes, because inverses are used.
You multiply by 2 and 3, then divide by 6

Reflect

10 Students' own answers, for example, 'I can make the calculation easier by working without decimals and then dividing and multiplying by powers of 10 to get my answer to the correct place value.'

6.4 Ratio and proportion with decimals

1 a 2 : 5 **b** 4 : 13 **c** 4 : 7 **d** 50 : 11
  e 3 : 5 **f** 9 : 25 **g** 3 : 5
2 a £384 and £615 **b** 128 : 205
  c £384 and £615 **d** Students' own answers.
3 8 : 5 : 7

4 a i £1 : €1.145
      ii €1 : £0.87
      iii The ratio of £1 to euros.
   b i £1 : $1.58
      ii $1 : £0.63
      iii The ratio of $1 to pounds.

5 48 cm

6 a 1 : 4   b 1 : 6   c 1 : 4

7 a 0.75 : 1   b 43 : 1

8 a Offer A 1 : 15, Offer B 1 : 18
   b Offer A
   c It makes it easier to make comparisons.

9 a Dylan 1 : 4.5, Sarah 1 : 3.33
   b Sarah's drink was stronger.

10 Earth 1 : 1067, Mars 1 : 5280,
    Mercury 1 : 7394

11 a June 1 : 1.67, July 1 : 2.
    b July had the higher proportion of children.

12 a 2.5 : 1   b 2.5 times   c 205 times

Reflect

13 a When the simplest form of a ratio is greater than the
       number you are sharing into a ratio. For example, when
       partitioning 20 in the ratio 5 : 37, it might be easier to use
       the ratio 0.12 : 0.88.
    b When the sum of the total parts of the integer ratio makes
       it easier to share the amount. For example, 0.2 : 3 might
       be easier as 2 : 30 because you only have to divide by 32
       instead of 3.2.

6 Extend

1 Afrah should buy the coat and pay for the shipping herself as it
   will cost £75.30, which is cheaper than £80.

2 a 2 700 000 000 is the largest.
   b Repeating without rounding makes the answer larger,
      because each number was always rounded down.

3 It is possible if P and Q are 2 and 5.

4 4.2282

5 a 0.026 hours
   b 0.64 pages
   c 38.5 pages
   d 250 pages
   e 7.5 books
   f 10 books

6 Multiple answers possible, for example 9 and 14.

7 0.6

8 £35.10

Investigation

9 Students' own answers.

Investigation

10 Students' own answers and pictures.

Reflect

11 Students' own answers.

Unit 7 Lines and angles

7.1 Quadrilaterals

1 a $a = 110°$, $b = 4\,cm$
   b $m = 90°$, $n = 12\,cm$
   c $p = 60°$, $q = 120°$, $r = 4\,cm$
   d $x = 40°$, $y = 140°$, $z = 6\,m$

Investigation

2

Quadrilateral	Diagonals bisect each other	Diagonals bisect the interior angles	Diagonals cross at right angles
square	✓	✓	✓
rectangle	✓		
parallelogram	✓		
rhombus	✓	✓	✓
kite			✓

3 a $e = 90°$, $f = 45°$
   b $p = 6\,cm$, $q = 8\,cm$
   c $x = 40°$, $y = 90°$
4 a i Trapezium
      ii $b = 50°$ (angle sum of a quadrilateral)
   b i Arrowhead
      ii $f = 25°$ (line of symmetry or pair of equal angles),
          $g = 210°$ (angle sum of a quadrilateral)
   c i Rectangle
      ii $k = 80°$ (vertically opposite angles),
          $l = 100°$ (angles on a straight line),
          $m = 40°$ (isosceles triangle), $n = 50°$ (isosceles triangle
          or right-angled triangle)
   d i Rhombus
      ii $p = 20°$ (isosceles triangle), $q = 20°$ (alternate angles)
          $r = 140°$ (line symmetry or opposite angles of a
          rhombus are equal)
5 Square
6 a A rectangle is a special type of parallelogram.
   b Students' own answers, for example,
      'A rhombus is a special type of parallelogram.'
7 For example, rectangle, square, trapezium,
   parallelogram, rhombus.
8 a $a = 30°$, $b = 15°$
   b $c = 45 - 15 = 30°$
   c

Number of rhombuses	1	2	3	4	5
Total angle	45°	75°	105°	135°	165°

   d Add 30°
   e 12 rhombuses.
9 The angle at the centre = 360 ÷ 6 = 60°, so the largest angle in
   each trapezium is 360° − 60° − 90° − 90° = 120°.
   So $a = 180° - 120° = 60°$ (angles on a straight line).

Reflect

10 If you know it is a kite, you can use all the properties of a kite
    such as angle sum, equal side lengths and lines of symmetry,
    and that the diagonals intersect at right angles.

7.2 Alternate angles and proof

1 a 51°   b 142°
2 Angles with the horizontal are:
   stage 1 − 3.5°, stage 2 − 6.5°, stage 3 − 4°
   Stages 1 and 2 are OK, but stage 3 isn't, so the ramp does not
   meet the recommendations.
3 Yes, they could be, as the angles could be the same
   size within 5°.

4 a $w = 180° - z$
   b $z = 180° - (x + y)$
   c $w = 180° - z$ (angles on a straight line).
      $z = 180° - (x + y)$ (angles in a triangle).
      $w = 180° - (180° - (x + y))$
      $w = x + y$
5 a i $w = 180° - x$ ii $z = 180° - w$
   b $w = 180° - x$ (angles on a straight line)
      $z = 180° - w$ (angles on a straight line)
      $z = 180° - (180° - x)$
      $z = x$
6 a Yes, because the alternate angles are equal.
   b No, because the alternate angles are not equal.
   c Yes, because the alternate angles are both 132°.
   d Yes, because the alternate angles are both 63°.
7 $q + r = 180°$ (angles on a straight line).
   $r + p + 90° + 90° = 360°$ (angles in a quadrilateral).
   $r + p = 180°$
   $r = 180° - p$
   $q + (180° - p) = 180°$
   $q - p = 180° - 180°$ so $q = p$.

Reflect

8 Ravi has only shown that they do for those triangles. To prove
   it, Ravi would have to look at a general case and show that the
   result is true even when you don't know any of the numbers.

7.3 Angles in parallel lines

1 a $c = 145°$ (corresponding angles)
      $d = 35°$ (angles on a straight line)
   b $e = 25°$ (vertically opposite angles)
      $f = 155°$ (angles on a straight line)
      $g = 25°$ (vertically opposite angles or alternate angles)
      $h = 155°$ (corresponding angles or angles on a straight line)
   c $p = 115°$ (corresponding angles)
      $q = 65°$ (angles on a straight line)
      $r = 65°$ (alternate angles or angles on a straight line)
      $s = 115°$ (vertically opposite angles or angles on
      a straight line)
      $t = 70°$ (vertically opposite angles)
      $u = 110°$ (angles on a straight line)
      $v = 70°$ (corresponding angles)
      $w = 110°$ (angles on a straight line or
      corresponding angles)
2 a $a = 45°$ (alternate angles)
      $b = 25°$ (alternate angles)
      $c = 110°$ (angles on a straight line)
   b $j = 50°$ (alternate angles)
      $k = 95°$ (angles on a straight line)
      $l = 35°$ (vertically opposite angles or angles on
      a straight line)
      $m = 145°$ (angles on a straight line)
   c $p = 115°$ (alternate angles and angles on a straight line or
      co-interior angles)
      $q = 100°$ (alternate angles and angles on a straight line or
      co-interior angles)
   d $w = 130°$ (alternate angles)
      $x = 110°$ (angles at a point)
      $y = 110°$ (alternate angles)
      $z = 120°$ (angles at a point)
3 a Vertically opposite angles.
   b d (alternate angles)
   c c (alternate angles)
4 a Angle $DCE = 47°$ (vertically opposite angles).
      Angle $CDE = 74°$ (alternate angles).
      Angle $CED = 59°$ (alternate angles).
   b

5 a $p = 125°$ (alternate angles)
$q = 55°$ (angles on a straight line)
$r = 55°$ (angles on a straight line)
$s = 125°$ (alternate angles)
  b Opposite angles of a parallelogram are equal.

6 $a = 50°$ (angles on a straight line with $40° + 90°$)
$b = 50°$ (alternate angles with a)
$c = 130°$ (angles on a straight line with a)
$d = 50°$ (vertically opposite angles with b)
$e = 140°$ (corresponding angles with $90° + 50°$)
$f = 140°$ (vertically opposite angles with e)
$g = 40°$ (corresponding angles with $40°$)

7 That all three lines BC, AE and FG are parallel, so that there are alternate angles between the top and bottom parallel lines.

Investigation

8 a i $b = 70°$, $c = 70°$, $d = 110°$
  ii $b = 160°$, $c = 160°$, $d = 20°$
  b i $a + b = 180°$, $c + d = 180°$, b and c are equal, a and d are equal.
  ii $a + c = 180°$, $b + d = 180°$
  c They add up to 180°.
  d Yes because co-interior angles in parallel lines add up to 180°.
  Students' own diagrams

Reflect

9 Work out the size of any angle, as there are links between different angles and calculating one lets you calculate another, which might help you work out the one you need.

7.4 Exterior and interior angles

1 a $a = 120°$
  b $b = 120°$
2 15
3 a 120°
  b 140°
4 a 165°
  b $360 ÷ 15 = 24$
5 Callie is correct. 1500 is not a multiple of 180.
A 10-sided polygon has total interior angles of
$8 × 180 = 1440°$
An 11-sided polygon has total interior angles of
$9 × 180 = 1620°$
6 a $x = 135°$
  b $y = 45°$
7 a 12°
  b 168°
  c Students' own opinions, for example:
  'Exterior because there are fewer steps and possibly simpler calculations'.
8 6°
9 a $a = 150°$ (interior angles of squares are 90°, interior angles of equilateral triangles are 60°, angles around a point)
  b $b = 150°$ (interior angles of squares are 90°, interior angles of hexagons are 120°, angles around a point)
  c $c = 108°$ (interior angles of decagons are 144°, interior angles of pentagons are 108°, angles around a point)
  d $d = 120°$ (interior angles of dodecagons are 150°, interior angles of squares are 90°, angles around a point), $e = 90°$ interior angles of dodecagons are 150°, interior angles of hexagons are 120°, angles around a point)
10 $y = 48°$
11 An equilateral triangle
12 Yes; as the interior and exterior angles add to give 180°, the only possibility is interior angle = 120° and exterior angle = 60°, which gives a regular hexagon.
13 16
14 12
15 a An equilateral triangle.
  b 45°

Reflect

16 Students' own answers, for example:
'The exterior angle measures the turn from one side around to the next side, and since you return to the same place it will be as though you have completed a full turn.'

7.5 Solving geometric problems

1 $720° − 90° − 90° = 540°$
$x = 540° ÷ 4 = 135°$ (two lines of symmetry).
2 a $x = 16°$
  b $2x = 32°$, $3x + 10° = 58°$, $32° + 58° + 90° = 180°$
  c $y = 122°$
3 $\angle CDE = 135°$

4 $\angle BAD = 40°$ (angles in a triangle)
$\angle BAC = 10°$ ($\angle BAC = \frac{1}{4} \angle BAD$)
$\angle CAD = 30°$ ($40° − 10° = 30°$)
$\angle ACD = 180° − 30° − 50° = 100°$ (angles in a triangle)

5 $x + y + 90° + 90° = 360°$ (angles in a quadrilateral)
$x + y = 180°$
$x = 120°$, $y = 60°$ (angle x is double angle y)
6 $x = 90°$, $y = 60°$ Students' own working and reasoning.
For example:
Angles in a pentagon make 540° //
$85° + 130° + x + 115° + (180° − y) = x − y$
$= 30$,
$2x = 3y$

Investigation

7 a The regular pentagon has rotational symmetry.
  b i 5   **ii** 72°   **iii** 54°
  iv Interior angle = $2x = 108°$
  c i 6   **ii** 60°   **iii** 60°   **iv** 120°
  d Interior angle = $180° − 360° ÷ n$, where n is the number of sides of the shape.

8 124°
9 140°
10 A triangle or a hexagon.

Reflect

11 a Yes, there are lots of ways.
  b Students' own answers.

Extend

1 $b = 230°$
2 a Yes, because $120° + 120° + 120° = 360°$, so three hexagons together will make a full turn.
  b Because 108° is not a factor of 360° so will not be able to make a full turn.
  c Squares and equilateral triangles.
3 30°
4 12, 1800, 30
5 a 74°
  b Square, pentagon, hexagon
6 The exterior angles of a polygon sum to 360° because they show the angle of turn to the next side. But in this diagram, two sides have two angles of turn shown, so the sum will be greater than 360°.
7 No, they are not parallel because AB meets the line at 51° but CD meets the line at 73°.
8 110°

Investigation

9 a 4 times: decagon, 5 times: 12 sides, 6 times: 14 sides, 8 times: 18 sides, 9 times: 20 sides, 10 times: 22 sides.
  b The ratio between the size of one interior angle and the size of one exterior angle increases by 0.5 for each additional side. This gives the pattern $0.5n − 1$.

Reflect

10 Students' own answers, for example:
'List the angle facts and look through the problem to see where I might use them.'

Unit 8 Calculating with fractions

8.1 Ordering fractions

1. $\frac{2}{5}, \frac{1}{2}, \frac{4}{7}, \frac{5}{8}$

2. Yes, because if the numerators are the same, then the larger the denominator, the smaller the fraction.

3. a   i $\frac{1}{2}$ ii $\frac{2}{7}$ iii 2   iv $\frac{3}{2}$

   b $\frac{2}{7}, \frac{1}{2}, \frac{3}{2}, 2$

4. Multiple answers, for example, $\frac{4}{4} > \frac{2}{8} < \frac{1}{3}; \frac{2}{8}, \frac{1}{3}, \frac{4}{4}$

5. a $\frac{3}{4}$ b $\frac{5}{6}$ c $\frac{7}{8}$ d $\frac{4}{5}$

6. a   i $\frac{2}{15} = \frac{1008}{7560}, \frac{3}{8} = \frac{2835}{7560}, \frac{12}{27} = \frac{3360}{7560}, \frac{4}{7} = \frac{4320}{7560}$

   $\frac{2}{15} = \frac{12}{90}, \frac{3}{8} = \frac{12}{32}, \frac{12}{27}, \frac{4}{7} = \frac{12}{21}$

   ii $\frac{17}{36} = \frac{34}{72}, \frac{11}{18} = \frac{44}{72}, \frac{8}{12} = \frac{48}{72}, \frac{23}{24} = \frac{69}{72}$

   $\frac{17}{36} = \frac{34408}{72864}, \frac{11}{18} = \frac{34408}{56304},$

   $\frac{8}{12} = \frac{34408}{51612}, \frac{23}{24} = \frac{34408}{35904}$

   b The best method is the one that uses the set of numbers that have the most common factors and the easiest lowest common multiple.

7. Multiple answers possible, for example,

   $\frac{1}{2} > \frac{2}{5} > \frac{3}{8} > \frac{4}{11} > \frac{5}{14}$

8. $\frac{6}{7} = \frac{12}{14}$, which is greater than $\frac{11}{14}$.

9. $-\frac{3}{8}, -\frac{1}{4}, -\frac{1}{3}$

10. $-\frac{3}{4}, -\frac{5}{8}, -\frac{1}{2}, -\frac{3}{7}$

11. Multiple answers possible, for example, $-\frac{3}{4} > -\frac{8}{2} < -\frac{1}{3}$;
    $-\frac{8}{2}, -\frac{3}{4}, -\frac{1}{3}$

12. Multiple answers, for example, $a = 3, b = 8, c = 4$
13. Multiple answers, for example, $a = 3, b = -2, c = 2$
14. No, for example $\frac{8}{7} > \frac{9}{8}$
15. Less, because the new fraction is two-thirds of the original fraction.
16. The new fraction is larger if the denominator is greater than 10.

Reflect

17. It is best to find a common denominator or numerator when there is an easy lowest common multiple to aim for.
    It is better to compare with an 'easy' fraction when there is not a simple lowest common multiple or when they are fractions that you are familiar with and can recognise their relative sizes.

8.2 Adding and subtracting fractions

1. a Any one of:

   $\frac{7}{10} + \frac{27}{30} = 1\frac{3}{5}$ $\frac{7}{10} + \frac{5}{12} = 1\frac{7}{60}$

   $\frac{7}{10} + \frac{11}{15} = 1\frac{13}{30}$ $\frac{27}{30} + \frac{5}{12} = 1\frac{19}{60}$

   $\frac{27}{30} + \frac{11}{15} = 1\frac{19}{30}$ $\frac{5}{12} + \frac{11}{15} = 1\frac{3}{20}$

   b $\frac{27}{30} + \frac{11}{15} = 1\frac{19}{30}$

   c Any one of:

   $\frac{27}{30} - \frac{7}{10} = \frac{1}{5}$ $\frac{27}{30} - \frac{5}{12} = \frac{29}{60}$

   $\frac{27}{30} - \frac{11}{15} = \frac{1}{6}$ $\frac{7}{10} - \frac{5}{12} = \frac{17}{60}$

   $\frac{11}{15} - \frac{7}{10} = \frac{1}{30}$ $\frac{11}{15} - \frac{5}{12} = \frac{19}{60}$

   d $\frac{27}{30} - \frac{5}{12} = \frac{29}{60}$

   e Students' own answers, for example, 'I used a common denominator to compare the fractions.'

2. a $1\frac{11}{20}$ b $\frac{3}{4}$ c $\frac{3}{10}$

3. $\frac{107}{120}$

4. a $\frac{3}{8}$ b $\frac{1}{2}$

   c £35 001–£55 000

   d For example, 'The wage categories are different sizes.'

5. a $\frac{2}{5}$

   b 30, as the LCM of 15, 10 and 6 is 30, and a normal class size is around 30 students.

6. 7 : 18

7. a

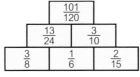

   b

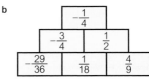

8. a   ii $\frac{1}{110}$ iii $\frac{1}{22}$ iv $\frac{1}{111}$

   b   i   ii

   iii   iv

Investigation

9. a Add 1 to the denominator to get the denominator of one of the unit fractions. For the denominator of the other unit fraction, multiply the first two denominators.

   b Multiple answers, for example, $\frac{1}{10} + \frac{1}{40}$.

Reflect

10. Students' own answers, for example, 'If I needed to get a smaller answer than one of the two numbers I was adding, I knew that the missing number had to be negative. If I was looking for a missing positive number, I subtracted the lower brick from the higher. If I was looking for a missing negative number, I subtracted the higher brick from the lower and then knew that my answer would be negative.'

8.3 Multiplying fractions

1. $\frac{1}{8}$

2. a −1   b 1   c 1
   d 1   e Students' own answers

3. a $\frac{4}{49}$ b $-\frac{8}{343}$ c $\frac{1}{28}$ d $-\frac{1}{98}$

4. a $\frac{1}{2}$

   b The writer gets £1000, the singer gets £250 and the guitarist gets £250.

5. a $\frac{35}{72}$ b $\frac{1}{32}$

6. a $\frac{1}{3}$ cm   b $\frac{8}{27}$ cm³   c $\frac{1}{4}$ m

7. a   i £5   ii £5

   iii They are the same; $\frac{1}{6}$; multiply them.

   b   i £24   ii £24   iii $\frac{3}{10}$; multiply them.

   c Yes

8 $\frac{3}{10}$

9 $\frac{1}{7}$

10 $\frac{5}{4}$

Investigation

11 a $\frac{1}{2}$ **b** $\frac{1}{2}$

    c 1 – fraction off normal price.
Then multiply by (1 – fraction off sale price).

Reflect

12 a Yes, because you are finding a fraction of a positive number.

    b No, because the answer will be closer to 0, so it will be greater than the original number.

8.4 Dividing fractions

1 $12 \div \frac{2}{5} = 30$, $13 \div \frac{1}{2} = 26$, $15 \div \frac{5}{7} = 21$,

$18 \div \frac{3}{4} = 24$, $30 \div \frac{5}{6} = 36$

2 a 1

    b No; you cannot divide by 0. $1 \div 0$ is undefined.

3 20

4 a Yes; Arthur's method always works because it uses the idea of the relative sizes of the two fractions.

    b Students' own answers.

5 24

6 Students' own answers, for example $\frac{1}{3} \div \frac{1}{2}$, $\frac{4}{15} \div \frac{2}{5}$ and $\frac{4}{9} \div \frac{2}{3}$.

7 $\frac{6}{\left(\frac{9}{2}\right)} \div \frac{4}{3} = 1$

8 $\frac{2}{5}$ cm

9 $\frac{6}{5}$ cm

10 $-\frac{1}{24}$

11 Multiple answers, for example, $\frac{5}{3}, \frac{4}{6}, \frac{1}{3}$

12 a $x = \frac{3}{8}$ **b** $x = \frac{1}{3}$ **c** $x = \frac{8}{6} = \left(\frac{4}{3}\right)$

13 $\frac{45}{56}$

14 It is never true.

Reflect

15 Students' own answers, for example,
'I multiplied by the reciprocal instead of working out a division of fractions.'

8.5 Calculating with mixed numbers

1 $-\frac{3}{2}$ or $-1\frac{1}{2}$

2 $2\frac{5}{6}$ m²

3 a 22 **b** 5 cm

4 a 8 **b** $8\frac{17}{20}$ **c** $17\frac{8}{9}$

5 a $12\frac{2}{3}$ m **b** $11\frac{11}{20}$ m

6 $23\frac{13}{30}$

7 $5\frac{250}{533}$

8 $3\frac{1}{6}$ cm²

9 $1\frac{11}{20}$

10 Any number between (but not including) $-1\frac{1}{2}$ and 0

11 a $10\frac{2}{5}$ **b** $21\frac{2}{5}$ **c** $5\frac{3}{5}$ **d** $1\frac{52}{73}$

Investigation

12 a $11\frac{1}{4}$ m²

    b The current largest rectangle will either be a $\frac{3}{4}n \times \frac{3}{4}n$ square (area $\frac{9}{16}n^2$), or an $\frac{3}{4}n \times \frac{3}{4}(n-1)$ rectangle (area $\frac{9}{16}(n^2 - n)$), where n is the number of panels in the longest side of the rectangle. Adding an extra two lengths will increase the maximum area by $\frac{9}{16}n$.

    c It will always increase by the number of panels in the longest side of the rectangle multiplied by the square of the fraction.

Reflect

13 Students' own answers, for example,
'I used inverse operations to work backwards through the calculations to find the original number. I used improper fractions to make the calculations easier. I used my knowledge of negative numbers to know when a calculation would give a negative answer.'

8 Extend

1 a $\frac{1}{4}$ **b** $\frac{7}{16}$

    c

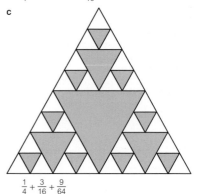

$\frac{1}{4} + \frac{3}{16} + \frac{9}{64}$

    d The term-to-term rule for the numerator sequence is '×3', first term is 1.
The term-to-term rule for the denominator sequence is '×4', first term is 4.

    e No, there will always be some white in the gaps.

Investigation

2 a $\frac{734}{21}$ cm² **b** Students' own answers

3 1875 m³

4 $\frac{adf}{bce}$

5 53

6 a $\frac{15}{16}$ **b** $\frac{45}{64}$

    c No; the terms will get increasingly smaller, but will never reach zero.

7 3 m

8 Yes, for example $a = 4$, $b = 2$, $c = -9$, $d = 3$

Investigation

9 a $\frac{7}{12}$ **b** $\frac{47}{60}$ **c** $\frac{37}{60}$

    d The answers are tending towards $\frac{7}{10}$.

Reflect

10 Students' own answers, for example,

    a 'The same, as they work in the same way'.

    b 'Improper fractions, because they work like fractions; with mixed numbers you have to check that the fraction part of the calculation works'.

    c 'Positive fractions and mixed numbers, because you don't have to think about the sign of your answer'.

Unit 9 Straight-line graphs

9.1 Direct proportion on graphs

1 a

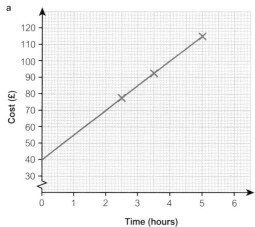

b £40.00
c £15.00
d No, the graph does not go through the origin.

2 a i £25   ii £32
b 1.6 GB
c No. The graph for A is a straight line through the origin, so data use is in direct proportion to the cost, but the graph for B does not go through the origin, so data for plan B is not in direct proportion to cost.
d Students' own graphs going through the origin, for example,

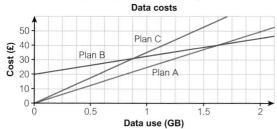

e Choose Plan A if data use below 1.6 GB and Plan B if use above 1.6 GB.

3 a Yes, because the line will go through the origin and will have a constant gradient.
b, c i

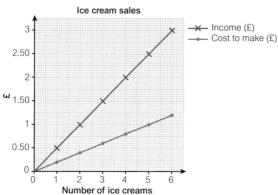

ii Yes, it is in direct proportion still.

Number of ice creams	1	2	3	4	5	6
Profit (£)	0.30	0.60	0.90	1.20	1.50	1.80

iii

d i No because it will not go through the origin now; instead it will start at £300.
ii 40 hours

4 a

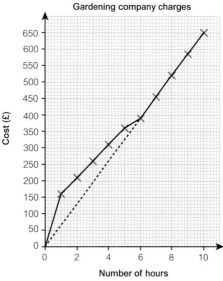

b If more than 5 hours of work is done, it is in direct proportion.

5 a Because it does not go through the origin.
b

Time (hours)	0	0.5	1	1.5	2
Distance travelled (km)	0	5	10	15	20

c

Ginny's run

d

Time (hours)	0	0.5	1	1.5	2
Distance between Ginny and Ben (km)	4	4.5	4	5.5	6

e No, it is not directly proportional because although the distance between them is increasing at the same rate it does not go through the origin.

6 Yes, because C varies with B and if B varies with A, then C will also vary with A.

Investigation

7 Never, the proportion between perimeter and area varies.

8 a No. Volume is directly proportional to the cube of the edge length: if you double the length, the volume multiplies by 8.

b Yes. Perimeter = k × edge length, where k is the number of sides.

c No. Area is directly proportional to the square of the base length.

Reflect

9 Students' own answers, for example

'When ordering things to be delivered, after a certain point you do not have to pay postage, so they are in direct proportion after that point but not before'.

9.2 Gradients

1 a i Yes   **ii** No   **c** No   **d** Yes

b

i
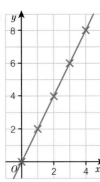

ii
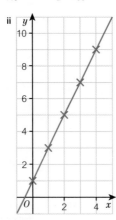

iii
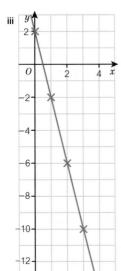

iv
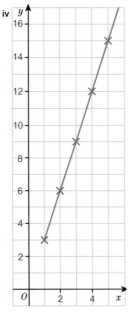

2 a The graphs showing direct proportion give a constant answer.

b If the graph shows direct proportion, the gradient is the same as the answer to the division.

3 a, b i, g i

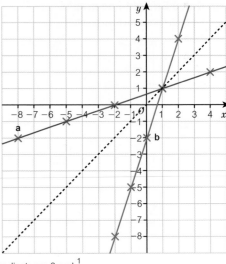

ii Gradients are 3 and $\frac{1}{3}$

c, d i, g i

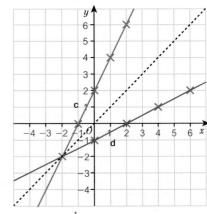

ii Gradients are 2 and $\frac{1}{2}$

e, f i, g i

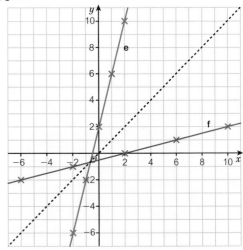

ii Gradients are 4 and $\frac{1}{4}$

g Gradient in each case is 1

4 a

x	−2	−1	0	1	2
y-values (A)	−3	−1	1	3	5
y-values (B)	2	1.5	1	0.5	0

b A: 2, B: $-\frac{1}{2}$

c The lines are perpendicular.

Investigation

5 a

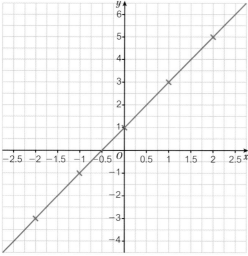

b 2

c No, the gradient is still 2.

d Students' own answers.

e Changing the y-values by the same amount has no impact on the gradient. It just moves the line up or down.

f Yes, the gradient is now 6.

g Students' own answers.

h Multiplying the y-values by a constant multiplies the gradient by the same amount because the y-values are more stretched out.

i Yes, it is now 2.2.

j The gradient changes by the same percentage.

k It has the same impact as multiplying by a constant because increasing by a percentage is the same as multiplying by a decimal.

Reflect

6 a A because it could go through the origin as well as showing if you multiply one value by a number, you would need to multiply the other value by the same number to stay on the line.

b C, it has a gradient of 0.

c A has a positive gradient whereas B has a negative gradient.

9.3 Equations of straight lines

1 a

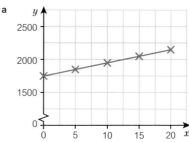

b £1750   **c** $y = 20x + 1750$

2 Parts **b**, **c** and **d** show direct proportion.

3

Equation of line	Gradient	y−intercept
$y = 2x - 5$	2	−5
$y = x + 1$	1	1
$y = 3x + 4$	3	4
$y = -x + 2$	−1	2
$y = -2x - 7$	−2	−7
$y = \frac{1}{3}x + 1$	$\frac{1}{3}$	1

Students' own graphs, with appropriate axes.

Any equation in the form $y = mx + c$ will have a straight line graph. m is the gradient and c is the y-intercept.

4 a (0, 10)   **b** £10   **c** 0.5   **d** £0.50

5 a, b

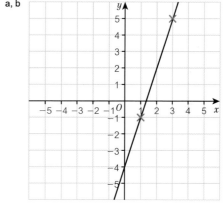

c $y = 3x - 4$

6 B: $y = 2x + 5$; C: $y = -\frac{1}{2}x + 4$; D: $y = -\frac{1}{2}x - 1$

7 a $y = -2x + \frac{1}{2}$

b, c, d, e

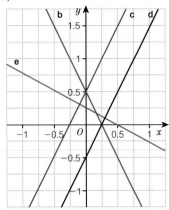

c $y = 2x + \frac{1}{2}$

d $y = 2x - \frac{1}{2}$

e $y = -\frac{1}{2}x + \frac{1}{4}$

f, h

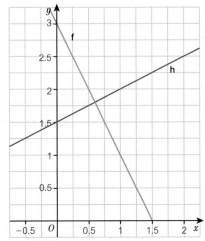

g They are parallel.

i They are perpendicular.

8 a True   **b** True   **c** True

   d False   **e** False

9 $y = 4x - 3$

Reflect

10 Students' own answers.

---

9 Extend

1 a −2   **b** $y = -2x - 3$

2 a

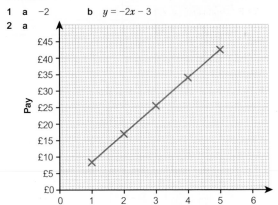

b £38.25

c No, because they would be paid a different amount for subsequent hours.

d Yes, the line would still cross the y-axis at 0.

e Yes, it would still cross the y-axis at 0.

3 a $y = \frac{1}{2}x + \frac{3}{2}$

b **i** $y = -\frac{1}{2}x - \frac{3}{2}$

     ii $(1, -2)$

c **i** $y = \frac{1}{2}x - \frac{3}{2}$

     ii $(-1, -2)$

d A translation of 3 units upwards.

4 a No, because it does not go through $(0, 0)$.

b

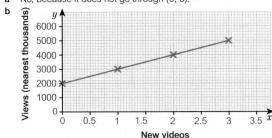

c $y = 1000x + 2000$ where x is the number of new videos and y is the number of views.

d No, because it is unlikely that the linear relationship will continue forever and the videos might get worse in quality.

e No, because it would be very unlikely for an exact number of extra views to happen for each extra video.

5 $y = 2x - 1$ and $y = -2x - 1$ $(0, -1)$

6 Yes, because that is the point that will stay the same when the graph is reflected.

7 Where the graphs intersect the x-axis.

8 $y = \frac{1}{2}x + 4$

Investigation

9 Students' own answers – any graphs which go through $(0. 0)$, i.e. the y-intercept is 0.

Reflect

10 Students' own answers, for example,

'In a science experiment or when planning for a business.'

Unit 10 Percentages, decimals and fractions

10.1 Fractions and decimals

1 a $2\frac{1}{2}$ hours b $\frac{3}{4}$ hours c $1\frac{1}{4}$ hours d $\frac{3}{10}$ hours

2 a 2 hours 30 minutes   b 18 minutes
   c 8 hours 12 minutes   d 1 hour 42 minutes

3 a $0.08\dot{3}$
   b 50 minutes = 10 × 0.08$\dot{3}$ = 0.8$\dot{3}$, which is still a recurring decimal.
   c Recurring: 5, 10, 20, 25, 35, 40, 50, 55 minutes.
      Terminating: 15, 30, 45 minutes.

4 Multiple answers, for example, 3 hours and 50 minutes.

5 0.7%, 1.1%, 1.4%, $\frac{1}{68}$, $\frac{3}{85}$, 4.1%, $\frac{1}{20}$, $\frac{4}{5}$, 0.$\dot{8}$

6
Flour	93 g
Butter	99 g
Sugar	105 g
Eggs	2
Vanilla	29 ml

7 a
Production line	Number of perfect scooters	Number of defective scooters	Fraction of scooters that are defective
A	460	40	$\frac{2}{25}$
B	543	57	$\frac{19}{200}$
C	370	30	$\frac{3}{40}$
D	279	21	$\frac{7}{100}$

   b i Production line D
      ii No; although it has the lowest proportion of defective scooters, it also has the lowest number of perfect scooters.
   c Yes; the proportion of defective scooters is the mean of the proportions for the four lines, and the total number of scooters produced (460) isn't too far from the actual mean (413).

8 a 0.7$\dot{6}$ b 0.5$\dot{6}$ c 6.$\dot{6}$ d 6.0$\dot{6}$

Investigation

9 a 0.333…, 0.444…, 0.555…, 0.666…,
      0.777…, 0.888…, 0.999…
   b 1.$\dot{4}$
   c i $\frac{37}{99}$ ii $\frac{65}{99}$ iii $\frac{6}{99}$

10 a 0.0$\dot{1}$ b 0.0$\dot{1}$$\dot{2}$ c 0.00$\dot{1}$ d 0.0$\dot{0}$1$\dot{2}$

Reflect

11 1.0909 is a terminating decimal; all the decimal places after the last 9 are 0.
    1.0$\dot{9}$ is a recurring decimal and has infinitely many repeating digits that alternate between 0 and 9.
    1.0$\dot{9}$ only repeats the 9 infinitely.

10.2 Equivalent proportions

1 The cake has a higher proportion of sugar.

2 Yes; in 2010 the rate was 78 per 1000 people.

3 a Councils B and C
   b Council A
   c Council A

4 a Jemma   b Alima

5 No; it falsely identified 2.6% of participants, which is higher than 0.1%.

6 The increase in sales from June 2017 to June 2018 is 77%.
   The increase in sales from July 2017 to July 2018 is 118%.
   118 is a 53% increase of 77, so the advert has had an effect on sales.

7 a Tigers because they score 1.29 goals per match compared to Bears with 1.2 and Penguins with less than 1.
   b Bears saved 54 goals, which is significantly more than either of the others.
   c Students' own answers, for example,
      'Penguins are the best because they have won the greatest proportion of their games.'

8 a United States
   b No, because we only know the proportions not the actual numbers of obese people.
   c i Females by 0.04%
      ii The second showed higher obesity rates in both men and women compared to the first study.

9 a A b > c
   b C (not enough information)

Reflect

10 Students' own answers, for example,
    'Write all the proportions as fractions with the same denominator, then compare the numerators. This would also work if you were comparing exactly two proportions. Or write all the proportions as percentages.'

10.3 Writing percentages

1 0.000 937 5

2 a £840
   b Cash price is cheaper by £40.

3 a £1320   b £120   c 10%

4 Multiple student answers, for example,
   'Find $\frac{1}{4}$ of the amount, or multiply the amount by 0.25, or find 10% then double that to get 20% and halve it to get 5%, then add 20% and 5%'.

Investigation

5 a Policy A: Emily pays £3000, Gary pays £6000 and Simra pays £15 000.
      Policy B: Emily pays £2000, Gary pays £6000 and Simra pays £18 000.
      Policy C: Emily pays £0, Gary pays £3000 and Simra pays £21 000.
      Policy C is best for Emily and Gary; Policy A is best for Simra.
   b Policy B is best for the Government in this case.

6 £1507.66

7 Any values that give the area of the blue triangle as 80 cm^2,
   For example, base = 10 cm, height = 16 cm,
   area = 0.5 × 10 × 16 = 80 cm^2

8
Year	Savings R Us		Gold savings		Investor's Delight	
	Interest	Total savings	Interest	Total savings	Interest	Total savings
1	4.3%	£834.40	5.1%	£840.80	4.8%	£838.40
2	4.3%	£868.80	5.1%	£881.60	4.8%	£876.80
3	4.3%	£903.20	5.1%	£922.40	4.8%	£915.20

The total amounts went up by the same amount each year because the accounts pay simple interest.

9 £14.73

10 a No
    b £100 × 0.9 = £90, £90 × 1.1 = £99

11 Students' own answers, for example:
    a i 'Find 25%, then divide by 2, or find 10% and 2.5% then add these together.'
       ii 'Find 15%, then divide by 2, or find 10% and 2.5% then subtract 2.5% from 10%, or find 2.5% and then multiply by three.'
       iii 'Find 35%, then divide by 2, or find 15% and 2.5% then add these together.'
       iv 'Find 65%, then divide by 2, or find 30% and 2.5% then add these together.'
    b i £225   ii £215   iii £235   iv £265.

12 Students' own answers

10.4 Percentages of amounts

1 Supermarket C gives the best offer.
Supermarket A: 1 biscuit costs 12p
Supermarket B: 1 biscuit costs 12.5p
Supermarket C: 1 biscuit costs 11.25p

2 a £1794.50
  b We don't know if they used the same amount of fuel.

3 11 million.

4 1 hour 48 minutes

5 £825

6 £300

7 The shop assistant does not realise that the percentage is a proportion of the amount. Georgia should only get 5% off the total amount.

Investigation

8 It will always work, because multiplication and division can be done in either order. Each time, you are multiplying the two numbers and dividing by 100.

9 a i 227 cm **ii** 207 cm
  b No, because the increase is compounded.

10 63 872

11 3528

12 Decreased by 1%

13 11%

14 a 1328 words
  b 1249 words
  c Mathematically, she will always write at least part of a word every day, but in practice she will eventually stop writing even one word a day.

Reflect

15 a First you would undo the increase of 10% by knowing you had 110% and using that to find 100%. Then you would undo the 5% decrease by knowing your answer was 95% of the original and using that to find 100% of the original.
  b You would still go back in reverse order, but you would start with 90% not 110% and then you would have 105% of the original amount.

10 Extend

1 £22.06

2 £50

3 a £313.05 **b** £365.25
  c

Year	Money at start of year	Interest rate	Money at end of year
1	£300	4.35%	£313.05
2	£313.05	4.35%	£326.67
3	£326.67	4.35%	£340.88
4	£340.88	4.35%	£355.71
5	£355.71	4.35%	£371.18

  d The amount with compound interest is greater than the amount with simple interest.

4 98 seconds

5 32

6 Yes, she did 24% better.

7 a In 2009 **b** Yes

Investigation

8 a $9x = 1.5$, so $x = \frac{1.5}{9} = \frac{15}{90} = \frac{1}{6}$
  b $x = 0.166666... = 0.16\dot{6}$
  c $1.\dot{6}$; after the first decimal place, the others didn't change.
  d $1.\dot{6} - 0.1\dot{6} = 1.5$; after the first decimal place, the others cancelled out.
  e $y = \frac{2}{9}$

f i $0.444444... = \frac{4}{9}$ **ii** $0.555555... = \frac{5}{9}$
  iii $0.777777... = \frac{7}{9}$ **iv** $0.888888... = \frac{8}{9}$
  v $0.999999... = 1$

9 a 71 : 50 **b** 71 oranges

Investigation

10 a i 50% **ii** 25%
  b Between 36 and 42 hours.
  c Tea: 24–30 hours.
    Diet fizzy drink: 30–36 hours.
    Fizzy drink: 24–30 hours.
    Energy drink: 36–42 hours.
  d Between 42 and 48 hours after first drinking the coffee.

Reflect

11 Students' own answers

Index

3D solids, 2D representations 21–2

addition, fractions 97–8
alternate angles 85–6
angles 83–94
  alternate 85–6
  corresponding 87–8
  exterior 89–90
  interior 89–90
  in parallel lines 87–8
area 15–18, 25–6
  parallelogram 17–18
  rectangle 15–16
  trapezium 17–18
  triangle 15–16

balancing method 55–6
bar charts 32, 38, 41–2
brackets 9–10, 47–8

capacity 26
coastline paradox 82
comparisons, data 37–8
compound interest 123
conversion graphs 59–60
correlation 39–40, 42
corresponding angles 87–8
count rates 72
cube roots 7–11
cubes (3D shape)
  surface area 23–4
  volume 19–20
cubes (power) 7–11
cuboids 19–20, 23–4
curved graphs 69–70

data, comparing 37–8
decimals 73–82
  calculations with 77–8
  division 77–8
  fractions and 115–18
  multiplication 75–8
  ordering 73–4
  percentages and117–18
  place-value calculations 75–6
  ratio and proportion with 79–80
  recurring 115–16
  terminating 115–16
deficient numbers 4
direct proportion 107–8
distance–time graphs 61–2
divisibility 3–4
division 3–4
  decimals 77–8
  fractions 101–2

elevations 21–2
equations 51–6
  balancing method 55–6
  one-step 51–2
  of straight lines 111–12
  two-step 53–4
estimation 2
expressions 45–50
  algebraic powers 45–6
  and brackets 47–8
  factorising 49–50
exterior angles 89–90

factorial numbers 4
factorising 49–50

fractions 95–106
  addition 97–8
  decimals and 115–18
  division 101–2
  mixed numbers 103–4
  multiplication 99–100
  ordering 95–6
  percentages 117–18
  subtraction 97–8
frequency tables 33–4

geometric problems 91–2
gradients 109–10
graphs 59–72
  conversion 59–60
  curved 69–70
  direct proportion 107–8
  distance–time 61–2
  equations of straight lines 111–12
  gradients 109–10
  linear 67–8
  line 37–8, 41–2, 63–6
  misleading 41–2
  non-linear 67–8
  real-life 67–8
  scatter 39–40, 42
  stacked proportion 68
  straight-line 107–14
grouped frequency tables 34

hectare 25
hexagons 89, 90
highest common factor 11–12, 49, 50

imperial measures 26
'in terms of' 51
index notation 11
index/indices see powers
interest 123
interior angles 89–90
inverse operations 55, 56
isometric paper 21

kites 16, 83–4, 91

line of best fit 39–40
line graphs 37–8, 41–2, 63–6
linear graphs 67–8
lines 83–94
  angles in parallel 87–8
  parallel 85–6
lowest common multiple 11–12

mean 33–6
measures 25–6
median 33–6
metric/imperial conversions 26
mixed numbers 103–4
mode 33–6
multiplication
  decimals 75–8
  fractions 99–100
multipliers 121–2

negative numbers 5–6
nets 21
nonagons 89
non-linear graphs 67–8
number 1–14
  calculations 1–2

octagons 89
one-step equations 51–2

ordering
  decimals 73–4
  fractions 95–6
overestimates 2

parallel lines 85–6
  angles in 87–8
parallelograms 17–18, 83–4, 88
pentagons 90, 91–2
percentages
  of amounts 121–2
  decimals and 117–18
  fractions and 117–18
  writing 119–20
pie charts 29–31
place-value calculations 75–6
plans 21–2
polygons 89–92
population pyramids 36
powers 7–12
  algebraic 45–6
prime factor decomposition 11–12
prime factors 11–12
prime numbers 4
proportions 79–80
  direct 107–8
  equivalent 117–18

quadrats 25
quadrilaterals 83–4, 91

range 35
ratio 79–80
real-life graphs 67–8
reciprocals 101
rectangles 15–16, 83–4
recurring decimals 115–16
rhombuses 83–4
roller coasters 62
roots 7–11
rounding 73–4

samples 25
scatter graphs 39–40, 42
Sierpinski's triangle 105
significant figures 73–4
square roots 7–10
squares 7–11, 83–4
stacked proportion graphs 68
statistics 29–44
stem and leaf diagrams 35–6
straight-line graphs 107–14
straight lines, equations of 111–12
subtraction, fractions 97–8
surface area
  cube 23–4
  cuboid 23–4

tables 32–4
terminating decimals 115–16
tessellation 93
time 115
trapezia 17–18, 83–4, 92
trends 65–6
triangles 90, 91
  area 15–16
truncation 74
two-step equations 53–4

underestimates 2
unit ratios 79–80
unitary method 121–2
units 119